ALL IN THE NAME OF LOVE

Edited by

Steph Park-Pirie

First published in Great Britain in 2004 by
POETRY NOW
Remus House,
Coltsfoot Drive,
Peterborough, PE2 9JX
Telephone (01733) 898101
Fax (01733) 313524

SB ISBN 1 84460 787 9

FOREWORD

Although we are a nation of poets we are accused of not reading poetry, or buying poetry books. After many years of listening to the incessant gripes of poetry publishers, I can only assume that the books they publish, in general, are books that most people do not want to read.

Poetry should not be obscure, introverted, and as cryptic as a crossword puzzle: it is the poet's duty to reach out and embrace the world.

The world owes the poet nothing and we should not be expected to dig and delve into a rambling discourse searching for some inner meaning.

The reason we write poetry (and almost all of us do) is because we want to communicate: an ideal; an idea; or a specific feeling. Poetry is as essential in communication, as a letter; a radio; a telephone, and the main criterion for selecting the poems in this anthology is very simple: they communicate.

CONTENTS

CAFFÈ LATTE

Carrying a cup of caffè latte
suddenly
I begin to mourn.
I set it down. Anniversaries
do not cut so suddenly, or so deep.

- the Bar Sistina, a bright morning
- so full of the day
as he would have been now
(and able to smoke here) - I cannot
swallow the croissant for tears.

Grief is such an ordinary thing,
a companion
that suddenly catches up,
not Ilium toppling, no great cry,
just a coffee smell, in a station bar.

Mary Armstrong

LUST

We sat together late one night, hugging and kissing, everything felt so right. I wanted more yet fought these urges wondering what would happen if I gave in.

I want to hold him and kiss him once more. Feel the closeness, which comes with caring or more. I know it can never be love but this devil called lust that tempts us to do more than kiss and caress.

Even now I see his smile and his eyes, which bore caring that night. But was it caring or am I mistaken, it could be lust yet one does not want to admit to this.

I want to hold him and kiss him once more. Feel the closeness, which comes with caring or more. I know it can never be love but this devil called lust that tempts us to do more than kiss and caress.

Experience in life makes a person face up to truths that there is more to life than love. We live for the moment and excitement is a major part of this. Seize the moment for you never know what the future holds.

I want to hold him and kiss him once more. Feel the closeness, which comes with caring or more. I know I can never be love but this devil called lust that tempts us to do more than kiss and caress.

Lisa Platts

RAZOR BLADE LOVE

Your razor blade love,
Those days I faced love,
Cutting to bleed,
Where did it all lead?

You took it all,
Kicked it like a ball,
And now you want more,
What is it all for?

You cannot win,
You struggle with your sin,
You will fall,
At the last hurdle.

We can't be pieced,
Will become breath deceased,
Soon we will die,
From this Earth fly.

Finding we were never to see,
Finding it just couldn't be,
I look at you compassionately.
How do you look at me?

I wrote your name everywhere,
Up, down, here and there.
Your name's on many a wall chalked,
Why couldn't we have talked?

Your razor blade love,
Those days I faced love.
How will we know,
Why all was so?

Carol Ann Darling

THE BIG FREEZE

I fell madly
Gladly, sadly
In love as
A boy,
When the lake
Used to freeze over.
She a skater:
It only took a glimpse,
She a little older but
That winter lasted forever.
She disappeared in my
Last year at school.
I've been waiting for
Heaven and Hell to
Freeze over ever since!

Alan Holdsworth

WISH

I wish I were a cloud that could just drift away
And decline to linger in a storm so fierce
I wish I could change like the butterfly changes
Into rapturous beauty
But not like the moon that waxes and wanes

I wish I were a flower untouched by the frost
But also untouched by the summer bee
For when the honey sooner or later is frozen
And to touch is to sting
The love between us is lost

I wish my heart were a stone that doesn't feel pain
Steadfast and resolute
And not like a chain of iron
That rusts in a nonchalant rain

I wish that your words were the edge of a knife
So that when you spoke them they cut your tongue
And when you swallowed they cut you to ribbons
Like they cut off my life

And I wish that my feelings were the bullets of a gun
So that when they hit you
You were destroyed inside
The likes of which cannot be undone
Such is your apathy
And rejection of me.

Louise Hulse

MY HEARTACHE DOESN'T FIT THE CRIME

I thought we had reconciled the past.
Our love throughout eternity would last.
But now you freeze me with an Arctic blast,
Then simply turn and walk away.
Loving you is like living in a danger zone.
Each step, one of regrets, into the dark unknown.
Perhaps it's better to live alone, than feel this way.
I say, 'The heartache doesn't fit the crime.'
You offer me no reprise, or try to compromise.
You reply, 'You are better on your own,
That I cut you to the bone,
With the things I say.
Thoughtless words I threw away,'
But they were never meant to hurt,
No more than when raindrops hit the dirt.
To land in some barren waste,
But that's all I have to face, without you,
Like winter trees, our love lies bare,
Stark and naked in the December air.
Who is to say who is right or wrong,
And what is fair on this grey and frosty day,
Like dying flowers, our love, the cold wind blew away.
Our summer passion burnt like a joyous flame,
Which was doused when the chill winds came.
Now in this Arctic waste, such a cold and lonely place,
This emptiness I embrace,
My heartache doesn't fit the crime.

Jonathan Pegg

WHAT IS LOVE?

Love is something that can grow from day to day,
It increases in time and whenever you give it away,
When you love each other you hold each other dear,
And as you grow older your love grows from year to year,
A mother loves her child in a different way,
Her love for her children is always there to stay,
A child loves its mother and its father too,
Although as the years go on they have to let them go,
Then the child gets married and has children of their own,
Soon you find that all at once another love has grown,
Grandparents love grandchildren as well as the happy pair,
That love never fades with time of that there is no fear,
The greatest love of all was shown by Jesus for our sin,
When he died and went to Heaven to let his people go in,
Yes love is something that no human eye can see,
But it is the greatest thing that there could ever be.

Stan Gilbert

TO LOVE AND LOVE AGAIN UNTIL AT LAST

I loved all, blindly, to eternity,
Not seeing any end, being in love,
But love was shattered, broken, vanity,
Lying at my feet, still, lifeless lost love,
Now fallen down a black abyss, unwove,
Unreachable again, such pain sustained,
Each born so bright, a shining star above,
Only to die at its brightest, reined,
Exploding into blackness love now drained,
An emptiness, a void, not filled or leapt,
With memories debris unleashed, remained,
A nebula of broken dreams not kept,
Each time catapulted from yesterday,
Until I found a lasting love to stay.

David M Walford

SOMETIMES YOU FEEL . . .

As I look through the eyes,
The eyes of my soul,
I find I leave my heart out,
To be hurt bruised or stole,
Sometimes you feel like,
Like love is suicide,
A pointed gun a painful burn,
A bottle in the tide.

David Cameron

FOR M

In words half murmured
In the shadow hours
We begin to weave
The fabric of our
Shared destiny
Each path chosen
Each decision made
Was a step
On the road that formed us
Bringing the threads
Of our lives
Together
To be woven anew.

Helen Ambler

VIRTUAL REALITY

Why buy real flowers?
Silk look almost alive,
except they're never
received with a kiss;
never know death.

Why wait for real love?
He can give you things
love cannot comprehend.
Big ring, big house, big bed -
with its mutually-agreed
exclusion zone;
cold, unwrinkled.

One day, sifting through
the detritus of a
previous life, you might
come across recorded smiles
that froze in summer suns;
mocking your ersatz years.
Unfading, unageing.
And you'll probably cry.

Alan W Ruffles

OTHER FISH

Your whiskers are like that of a walrus
You huddle with your mates in a shoal
Your bite is like that of a shark's
You blunder about like a gigantic whale

God I'm glad there's other fish in the sea.

Sharon Grimer

STRUCK

At the bus stop I did stand
Along came love and held my hand
Sorry I'm a late nice boy
Hand of mine tightened with joy
Please no worry or no fuss
Here is now the first bus
That was just a little lie
Eyes went up looking at sky
On the bus, took a seat
Huddled up and looking neat
She leaned, kissed me on my cheek
Couldn't talk, well just a squeak
A mortal blow from above
Shape of heart and of love.

Michael D Bedford

MY LOVE FOR YOU

I love you for so many things
I don't know where to start
I know this to be true
From the ache - when we're apart

You are the most whole person
That I have ever met
I love you for your dreams
And all you aim for yet

I love the way you cherish me
And the way you hold me dear
I want for no more
Than to have you always near

I love you for your laughing eyes
Your smile, your loving ways
This life we have together
Is perfect in every way

Today you have made me most happy
And it needs to be said
Though it is plain for all to see
Oh honey I love you
Yes I love the man I wed.

Bev Driffield

TONIGHT I WILL NOT LIE

The moment when your lips reach our for breath
And subtle kisses, crawls across my head
To strike me weak;
How can I love you, drowned in dreamland's death,
How can I know you, silent on the bed
If thoughts will never speak?

Our souls shut down like windows in a storm;
Tonight will come and go, so distantly,
I will not know you as I ever have.
No light will silhouette your lily form
To drive the passion in me, instantly.
I think of things you cannot give, but gave.

To think that I have ever held your hand
Is miracle enough to make me weep!
What have we to display that we designed
Alone? You are too far away to understand,
An image from a pale and tortured sleep.
You never could be born inside my mind.

Tonight I will not lie, but wander out
To think you over: should our act go on?
Probably not. If not, unbind our link.
My mind grows old, my heart is dark with doubt,
I wish this dreary act of farce was done.
But still before I speak, I stop; and think.

Chris Cotes

To My 'Heroic Failure' - NB

You were once my hero
I guess that you still are
And, though it's sometimes painful
I still care, from afar

You came when life was difficult:
I thought you understood,
And yet, you probably never did -
And what's more, never would

I loved you like a brother,
Adored your 'diff'rent' ways.
All I wanted was to thank you
For bright'ning up my days

I could see you had your troubles
- It's written in your eyes
I could tell you'd been hurt deeply:
- An insight you'd despise

Still, now, you probably hate me
But, as the years slip by
I wish more and more you'd asked me
- Not *assumed* the reason why . . .

S J Robinson

LOVER'S SILHOUETTE

It was a winter's night when love first met us frosted was the land.
The sky sparkled with many stars,
the cold was kept at bay by the warmth of passion.

Walking hand-in-hand we stopped beneath the hawthorn tree,
the stars twinkled in your eyes.
My heart raced upon our embrace we were lovers
silhouetted by the moonlight.

Our sense of togetherness is unequalled in the universe,
we fused as one, your kiss was electric the greatest pleasure
to behold me.

Our caressing was utopia we floated in celestial splendour,
whispers we shared of thoughts, rhymically entwined, locked
by the emotions of love.

Duncan Macfarlane

THE WEDDING OF GLEN AND SHIRLEY

We sang a hymn this morning in church
and it was called Such Love.
Such a beautiful song for such a beautiful occasion.
In everyone's life we give and take such love,
and in a perfect marriage such love is counted in caring for each other.
For every day of their married life now such love will be different,
different because it will be shaped by what they both think, say and do.
Such love awaits ahead for them both.
And as husband and wife a whole new adventure, and life, will unfold.
Life can sometimes be odd with its twists and turns,
face it, both with such love that is so strong,
work on it, with such love of understanding each other's needs.
If your hearts stay young you will always have dreams,
turn them into reality.
And I pray such love gives you both added years
to harvest all these dreams . . .
for such love extends from the cradle to the cross
today we ask you both as husband and wife
to put such love into your marriage.
Reach out for such love for he is easy to be found
Build on sure things that will endure life's tasks
from this beautiful day onwards,
so we, all here, give you both, such love.

Les Campbell

WHY DID I FALL?

I loved him for a while
and when I was dropped by him I felt empty and lost inside.
I pretended I hated him and didn't care
but deep down I still loved him and my heart started to tear.

Then a couple of months later my heart was healed,
until he clicked his fingers and I ran back straight away.
I got all my hopes up when he said he wanted me back
and let me down again and with his manipulating ways.

Amy Parker (16)

TIME TO SAY GOODBYE

Although it's time for me to say goodbye
I never really wanted to go
You will never see me cry
Even though I'm feeling so low

I love you more than words can say
My heart hurts more than you can see
But that'd the price I have to pay
For wanting a love that can never be

For you my heart will forever pine
Never will my heart be free like a dove
For my love you did decline
My everlasting love

I miss your smile and witty humour
And wish that you were here with me
Never before has my future looked doomer
Than when you said we would never be

Your love for me was not so strong
And this is something that I know
I've never loved someone for so long
This is why it's time to go.

Tanya Woodhouse

SHORT MEETING

I smile when you're beside me
    I want to hold your hand
I kiss your cheek so slightly
    You hug me where I stand
You tell me that you love me
    I'm forever in your heart
I want to grab you tightly
    'Cause I hate it when we part.

L Sheppard

TIME FOR LOVE

Oh would I spend an age upon your perfect face,
a further era on your body, full of grace.
Another aeon spent on your soft hair.
And on your legs so shapely, what a pair!
More years to see the smile upon your lips,
enticement in the way you move your hips.

I listen when you speak and hear no lies,
intelligence from a young mind - so wise.
And through the empty years I pray, my pet,
that from the pedestal, upon which you I've set,
you will glance downwards, from the height above,
for one brief second of your time and give me - love.

D G W Garde

BLUE BEDROOM EYES

When I first saw you I was mildly impressed
You were smoking, hungover and badly dressed
But your blue eyes scanned underneath what I wore
And my heart for six months wanted more.
'I think it was lust at first sight,' you said,
'You know what I'm saying is right,' you said,
'I've been thinking about you all night,' you said,
Though you slept in another's bed.
You kissed me, you held me and whispered you cared
But this time it was my bed you shared -
Then at my eighteenth which you dared to attend
Blue bedroom eyes saw another girl 'friend'.

You told other people you didn't know
Why I cried and they told you to go;
You told them my cries were all lies
And you spoke with your crystal blue eyes.
'This is such an unfair accusation,' you said,
'It was only a little flirtation,' you said,
'The whole thing's a fabrication,' you said,
It was you who was playing with my head.
You told me you cared when the saga begun
I hope you're happy, I hope you had fun,
I won't beg you to love me or ask you to stay
'Cause I'm stubbing you now in your own ashtray.

Gemma Alexander

WHY DID YOU HAVE TO GO AWAY?

Why did you have to go away?
A fissure in the granite rock,
A spring bursts forth and seems to mock,
Even a mountain, solid, strong
Gives in to pressure before long.
And like the rock, I too held fast
Until you said farewell at last,
To travel to a further shore,
Your homeland calls for evermore.

Long years have passed, I still feel pain,
Reminders bring their own refrain,
Sounds and scenes we used to share,
Exquisite moments, fragrant, rare.
My hope springs up from day to day,
Why did you have to go away?

Norma Rudge

LOVE IS THE STRONGEST EMOTION

Love is the strongest emotion,
Embracing the one you love,
Feeling the pain, when it comes to an end,
Trying to pick up the pieces again.

Love is the strongest emotion,
Feeling happy when he calls your name,
Knowing he feels the same.

Love is the strongest emotion,
Spending your life together,
Binding and entwining hearts,
Sometimes I wonder how it starts.

Love is the strongest emotion,
Committing your life forever,
In good old matrimony
Together,
Till eternity.

S Longford

The Way You Make Me Feel

It's the things that you do, the things that you say,
it's the way you pass me every single day.
It's the way that you smile, the way that you walk,
the way that you frown, the way that you talk.

I try to block you out of my mind,
I try to say that there's someone else to find.
I try not to like you,
but when I try, it just will not do.

I don't want to be responsible,
I don't want to make you miserable.
My heart is on fire, it's so flammable,
it's down to my desire, you're so irresistible.

What I can't hide,
is the feeling inside.
It's the way you make me feel, everything that you do,
I want to tell you, I'm so in love with you.

Dominic Ryan

OLD ACQUAINTANCE

Am I still your queen?
Your root?
Your breast?
Your source?

Your traipse over me
and your soles
sink tracks in the sand.

Soon when the wind blows
blind I shall be -

your footprints scattered like seed,
myself unable to follow,
my words my only lullaby.

I walked to you -
as a pilgrim towards a father,
as a nomad towards the sea

and I found
you were a mirage -
a chimera vapid and weak

 your centurion banner ash,
your sword as tenuous as silk.

Where, where is your tenderness?
Where, where is your strength?

N C Grant

SHATTERED

The life inside was overflowing,
Expanding and infolding . . .

I let you slowly inside,
These hard, restricted barriers of mine
Slowly,
Without my knowing,
You got in further,
Than I had planned . . .

I put on a facade,
To show I was strong,
That my feelings didn't run so deep,
But boy I was wrong!

As the problems in my life,
Started to rise and come to life,
I thought of the pain,
They would bestow on you,
And deep, down inside,
I knew this was something I could never do . . .

With a heavy heart,
I told you we're through,
And worried about you,
Constantly . . .

I knew you would be upset,
And I thought,
Possibly,
Deeply so . . .

But how wrong I was,
As your feelings had changed,
Your love has gone to someone else,
So quickly,
And unexpectedly,
That I wonder inwardly,
If you ever loved me after all?

I'm shattered deep inside,
The feelings I can no longer hide . . .

I sat outside,
In the rain,
Thought about things,
And realised I didn't ever want to see you again,
As you have caused me too much pain . . .

I don't blame my rock,
I never shall,
It is you I blame,
Though I have feelings still,
But they fade with the passing of night . . .

And there they shall stay,
A distant reminder . . .

As in time I shall feel nothing,
Only pity that I was sucked in,
By such an uncaring,
Hurtful person as you.

I hope you have a good life,
As my love for you will not last,
It's fading already,
Just as the evening pasts.

Eventually,
These feelings,
Will no longer be strong towards you,
But instead be nothing,
Just a reminder of a past mistake
An intrusion in my life . . .

Patricia Rowsell

BEAUTIFUL PLACES

In fields of green
Our love has been
In skies of blue
With rainbow hue
On tropical lands
We held our hands
We held our hands
In icy cold places
With red rosy faces
Amid soft snow drift
Our love also did sift
In Heaven, not yet
But it will, I bet
The beautiful scenes
Are not mere dreams?
As our love once more
Ever opens a door
But 'twas within
And surely not a sin
Our own two hearts
Where love did start.

C R Slater

THE FEELINGS

Never felt like this before
Never imagined it would happen at all
Never felt so secured
Never felt so comfortably embraced

That feel of innocence in you
That pride that makes you feel blue
The tingling feeling that comes with a touch
The happiness after a hug is much

The love that takes every problem away
The smiles that keep haters at bay
The eyes that shine through the heart
Even apart, the eyes reflect in the heart

The moments that felt like paradise
The voice with the sweetest advice
Though the situation is worrying at times
The memory that makes you as small as a mice

The love you feel is unexplainable
The warmth is unmeasurable
The future is more understandable
The love that makes the heart alarmable.

Ify Helen Nzegwu

I WOULD

I would pluck a flower from its bed
Just to see you smile
I would read poems from a book
If you would linger for a while

I would watch you move and flow along
Just to see your timeless grace
And keep the beauty in my heart
As I look upon your face

I would feel the beating deep inside
As I held you close to me
And wonder what may happen
If this is allowed to be

I would have your face the first thing I see
As I wake in morning light
And the last thing in my world
At the fall of night

I would look close and deep into your eyes
A powder shade of blue
And hope you return how I feel
If I say I love you.

Leslie Tomlinson

TELL ME IT'S NOT TRUE

Once was a moment I looked in your eyes,
To love like a dream to keep me awake,
Where even the night tries hard to disguise,
And even the day for you I would take;
I gave you the stars, I gave you the moon,
I gave you the night which fell to the earth,
I gave you the rose, where scent were the tune,
I gave you the sun and all it was worth;
So long were these hopes to wander until,
Eloped in the gathering years, became
Like lips to the wind, a kiss to fulfil,
And hearts were a destined for love to claim;
But love, will you to bless or show to me,
Look deep your heart and tell it cannot be.

Christopher W Wolfe

DESTINATION ZERO

The eyes across some crowded scene
Succeeding hope, perhaps a wish, but curiosity
Playful lips, a duel, preceding dreams
A smile silencing talking heads, intensity

Dilation, rush, electric space
Generating cocktail waves, wicked, frenzied chance
Music slow, seductive lines embrace
A meaning, moving, merging into trance

Conflict, nerves, sense and hormones vie
Deep breath before the smell test push
One word, one laugh, one sign, one sigh
A glass, a touch, a tell-tale blush

Euphoria, landslide relief, object secure
Conversation cool, no war, no sport, no slim-fast tea
Think ballet, theatre, cordon bleu
Politics and human rights providing they agree

Suggestion of a quieter place with softer light
A moonlit garden stroll amid night-scented stock
Crickets calling serenade throughout the night
Each blissful moment steals an hour from the clock

Disaster, wristward glance, the furrowed brow
O humour, where for art thou in this hour of need?
Blast your lips you ape for misinterpreting the 'now'
Smiling like a fool will never rectify the deed

Desperation, prospects dashed, love again on hold
Another doorstep 'text you soon now, cheerio'
How could such promise climax in a bed so cold?
A message in a rocket doomed for destination zero.

Michael William Molden

PAST IS PAST

He was a body builder
With rolling curly locks
Gorilla in the mist (well groomed)
He infiltrated an entire album
Sensitive of course despite appearances
He took it all too far
Love, hate, the standard emotions
Telephones bugged, hen-nights invaded
Flowers, enough to make his own wreath
An oversized Cupid with shining teeth
He was the negative that you cut out
Swaggered into your life
And staggered out
We know your love was misdirected
And Mr Ex remains affected.

Jason Stroud

MISCARRIAGE OF LOVE

When was the exact moment
of this supreme covenant?
A tiny sparkling seed then sown,
lay rested, comfortable, still, unknown.
But just as in fertile soil; has grown.

Still within that sheltering warm,
the tiny ray is quick to form.
As if the sun at early morn,
a new fresh life begins to dawn.
(But the rose cannot bloom without the thorn.)

One gentle kick and the dream is real.
A cherished response that the heart can feel.
Surely now the love is free,
to announce by loud decree;
its path leads on through eternity.

Care is sadly left behind
as Happiness prepares her blind.
This way has many a twist and bend.
The soft protection can no longer defend,
nor aid to the fading star lend.

Desperately the seed gives one more thrust;
to regain the friendship, loyalty and trust.
Wilted prematurely, the new bud dies.
Alone, isolated, cold it now lies,
leaving its sorrow in one pair of eyes.

Emptiness within those cradling walls
echoes round the barren halls.
The labour pains are felt the same,
to torture the mind, to wreck and blame
itself of killing the living flame.

Margaret Webster

LONELY WITHOUT LOVE

Lonely in a crowded room
Lonely with people passing to and fro
Lots of people chatting to you
But in your heart a dagger is thrown

Loneliness lives deep within
A heart that cries for company
I give a hug, but all you feel is sin
You need true hope, not plastic personality

One day your heart may feel strange
Repair itself and burst outward-bound
For loneliness is just a phase
Until a love can be found

The dagger may lift
A smile is born
From that lonely, crowded room
You'll eventually be torn.

S J I Sutton

HARD TO SAY

The words 'I love you' are so very hard to say,
When the one you love, doesn't think of you in the same way,
Because whenever they come near,
Your heart fills with such joyous cheer,
That you run out of things to talk about,
Making you appear like some gormless lout,
After going through all the possible scenarios in your mind,
There is only one winning solution you can find,
And that is to keep the feelings you have inside,
As to remain friends these emotions must hide,
So for this friendly relationship you must toil,
To keep control, of your inner turmoil.

Mark Redfern

Dawn's Break

Alas but now I must away my love for we must not be caught.
The night we stole and may again if we might just have thought.
My love for you is worth the risk I take this very morn.
'Tis a truth your kisses are so sweet I truly am reborn.

The night brought its own reward we have been paid in full.
But should I risk the sword again I would be such a fool.
I would take the punishment that they would give to me.
If 't meant that I could be in your arms I would never flee.

But rules are rules and we should wait until our wedding day.
I want you for my heart dictates . . . I do not have a say.
It pains me still to leave this way I'll miss you for a while.
But then you'll be in my arms again and serve me up a smile.

I love thee true, I love thee long, in death I'll love thee still.
'Tis true, not like the greatest meal, I'll never have my fill.
I tear away for they are near, if my choice I'd never go.
I leave you with the knowledge true that I do love you so.

Robbie Mackenzie

LOOKING FORWARD

May is a month when the sun does shine,
Even when cloudy I can see the sun above.
Every day will be sunny when you are mine,
When I can be near you and give you my love.

Please don't feel pressured, angered or pained,
Our love is for real and it's not long now,
'Til together as one, such harmony to gain,
This glorious love treading new ground.

Stella Rogers

A HONEYSUCKLE BLOOM
(Dedicated to Simon Ward, who is now my son-in-law!)

Thank you so much for bringing me,
a honeysuckle bloom,
it was the sweetest thing to do.
Sometimes no words are needed,
it meant the world to me,
I shall remember it dearly.

You have such beautiful qualities.
When smelling it in the garden,
whilst, I was in pain,
the air felt soft and warm,
I felt so lucky,
thinking I could be outside,
to feel and see sweetness,
all around me.

You brought some of that sweetness to me,
for such a beautiful thought,
I thank you!
I am so proud and glad,
that you will one day,
be part of our family.

My one wish,
is that you never loose,
such rare qualities and understanding,
that this world will never alter your spirit.
For there is truly, beauty inside of you!

Maria Ann Cahill

LOVE

A love in my heart
Is all I had.
When I'm with you
I'm sure you be glad,
Please don't be sad
I'm lost without a heart.
Be my heart
Don't let it be torn,
My heart will be broken.
If you break it
Please fix my heart
So your love can be in it.

Angela Cole

LOVE-HATE RELATIONSHIP

Parents . . .
    We hate them.
Siblings . . .
    We hate them.
Ourselves . . .
    We hate most.
Because no matter how nasty,
How much they make us cry,
Deep down we know they care.
Whilst on the surface it might not show,
And though we fight them all the way,
Someday, we know we'll miss them
And that they'll feel the same.

Amy McLaughlan (15)

MY LADY OF THE NIGHT

I'll dress you in a purple gown
With shawl of silken thistledown
And from the night, will take its stars,
Storing them in fine crystal jars.
They will become your lanterns, bright,
Leading you through the velvet night.

You sit on your obsidian throne,
Clear as black glass but only stone.
I'll catch the silvery moon for you;
Thread it upon a chain of dew
And place it around your neck so fair,
Then cast the moonbeams on your hair.
The sapphires of night hang from your ears
And I'll place on your head a crown of tears.

Soon you'll rest on cushions of mist
And the golden dawn, your face will kiss.
The magic you've spun holds me so tight,
Taking me through the dream-filled night.
My heart is captive, can ne'er be free.
Night Lady, you belong to me.

Hazel Mills

FROM HIM TO HER

I love the way you look tonight,
Your eyes are such a wonderful sight,
You are the one I love,
Your face is as white as a dove.

You look so lovely in a dress of lace,
And the pale white of your face,
I miss you so much when you go away,
But you have come back to me today.

Your lips are red like a rose,
And with your perfect nose,
Your hair is charcoal black,
You are the one I lack.

Your teeth are so white,
They shine like a light,
Your eyes are so blue,
I love you and I need you.

Claire Murray

GIRLS' NIGHT OUT

The working week is done, thank God! Time to put on my party gear,
gonna dance 'til I can't feel my feet and drink my body weight in beer.
It's the girls' night out tonight and I'm sure it will be fun,
drinking, laughing, partying and snogging everyone.
Knowing me I'll have too much, and pass out on the floor,
or go for a quick wee in the gents, and the lock will break on the door.
You can always guarantee one of us up singing karaoke really bad,
then it will be dares to kiss the most ugly looking lad.
I know I'll be the winner at that, as I can always find a minger,
much easier than karaoke, I never was much of a singer.
Then as the night comes to an end and most of us have been sick,
it's off to the fast food house to see what pizza we can pick.
As we're walking to the taxi rank singing Lulu's *Shout,*
it's off home to our beds 'til the next big girls' night out!

Nicola Pitchers

THOUGHTS

Long ago I dreamed a dream
I thought that I could be like a queen
I thought the world a lovely place
And days on earth were full of grace
No thought I had of growing old
I loved adventure and I was bold
Travelled the world, fancy free
No thought of future bothered me
The world was like a huge balloon
Drifting by with the silvery moon
In youth my world did seem young
All obstacles; I could overcome
Then wrinkles came with lines of age,
Thoughts of this world changed to rage
This world eternal still carries on
My mortal life will soon be gone
Am I to die and be born again?
My spirit once more to live and reign
To live again in human form
Be born a babe, man or woman
And do the things I have not done
So I speculate on life and love
Discover the answers if there's one?
Why meaningless like changing tides
Without a reason, we must abide.
Death so certain comes to us all.

Rich or poor it doesn't matter
Money cannot in any way
Prolong your existence one more day
A very puzzling universe
Baffles scientists around the earth
They can do clones of animals
Make having babies miracles
Yet find the secret of immortality
Beyond all their capabilities
I believe in Almighty God
Who sent His very blessed son?
To preach to us how things might be
When earthly life does have its key
The key to Heaven is within our reach
Give me this wisdom I beseech
Yet Solomon a mighty king
He too did die knowing everything.

J Prentice

DOWN MEMORY LANE

On the 4th of October we married
It was cold but the sun shone bright
We couldn't afford a honeymoon
So stayed in my mum's room that night
It was only nine weeks later
I gave birth to our first gorgeous son
I had just turned sixteen when I had him
You were just twenty-one
You worked all the hours God sent us
To buy us a home of our own
I ignored all the family warnings
That you'd leave me and our baby alone
They said we were too young to marry
And a baby would cause us more strain
I wished they'd have helped and encouraged us
But they just showed disgust and disdain
But I knew from the day that we met
Our love will always remain
It wasn't our baby that hurt us
It was family causing our pain
Although you worked many hours
To show them that you were a 'man'
Our first home was far from a mansion
Just a broken down old caravan
But to us it was Buckingham Palace
And I don't deny it was hard
We had no heating or water
Lived in an old muddy yard
But you didn't give up trying
I supported you all of the way
And I wanted to show all the family
We'd make it together some day

Now it's twenty-seven years later
We've two more children to add to our joy
A beautiful daughter
And another wonderful boy
We've a beautiful house that we dreamed of
In a marriage that's loving and strong
With so many of life's riches
So glad that our families were wrong
But I've never forgot where we started
And give thanks to God every day
As long as I have you and our children
They can take all our possessions away
For you are my rock and my soulmate
Our children are dear to my heart
I know we were young when we married
But nothing could keep us apart
My tummy still flips when I see you
I'm proud of the man you've become
I will love you forever my darling
You'll always be my number one.

Trudy Simpson

A GOLDEN PROMISE MADE

Red letters for my sweet rose,
Therefore, I needed to compose.
A song for my loving flower,
Dreams are kept, upon this silent hour.
Do you remember when we just met?
And the secret promises, we together kept.
To belong, solely to each other,
For I desire you alone, as my dear lover!
There's no need for a contract to hold,
For you bring in summer,
And turn base lead, into purest gold!

May we together grace each new day, we share,
As your every whim, becomes my only care.
I have become used to all your strange ways,
And God bless all of them, in our long days.
I hope we may grow old together,
And partake in strong fate, whatever the weather.
Soon I find a string of pearls, in your sparkling smile,
Which, always lasts, a long honeymoon while.
May we always hold on to such beautiful things,
While the sweet sound of our love, soars and sings.
To the happiness, found once again, on sweet Heaven and Earth,
As to the blessed wonders of life,
Please, let the whole world give in to love's sweet birth!

Victor Shaw

ABIDE WITH TIME

Why when love is so great,
Do I have to sit alone and wait.
I often stay at home,
Sitting by the telephone.

But the telephone doesn't ring,
Neither does the mocking bird sing.
Often the only thing I hear,
Is a clock ticking quite near.

Our love was built on faith and trust,
We always do what we must.
To lose you is what I fear,
Especially when you don't come near.

Your bond must be a thick chain,
As to her you still remain.
You say your love is all for me,
Am I so blind I cannot see.

All blindness that veils the heart,
Holds us, even when we are apart.
Now I have to abide with time,
Maybe one day you will be mine.

Margaret Upson

Fairy Love

My fairy lover, shimm'ring, starry Belle,
Eternal radiance, Queen of States Afar,
Enchantress, truly spirit avatar,
Romance's spirit netwise, druid's spell:
You lure my thoughts, my acts, my soul t' reel
Against that rigid cybernetic tsar.
Rejoicing I, upon your rising star
Of chance, am soaring in a mighty swell.
So immaterial, yet so real,
Asarcously designed of nulls and ones,
Of no substance, only thought objectified
Like Plato's perfect forms, your love ideal
Defines th' potential of all other loves.
Oh would you be my digitronic bride?

John A Mills

UNCONDITIONAL LOVE

Confusion,
Alien feelings
So strange and untrue,
Anger, frustration,
Sleep
A distant memory.
Tired arms reaching
Out to her,
Compassion spent
Patience worn.
A smile glued
To hide the fractures
But the tears fall
Regardless,
Awkward love
But bound by nature,
It's hard to forget
When you can't see the future.

Susan Andrews

ALONE

I will not pick up the phone
I will not ask him why
I will not weep anymore
I believe the lie.

I will buy a smile for my face
And wear it well
A shade of tranquil good grace
And who can tell?

And I will not give anymore
And I will not try
But not to live anymore
Can't be my style.

With my feet pressed to the floor
In polished shoes
I tell them 'vanquished amour'
Is a bag I choose.

But I can't laugh anymore
And I will not come
And I will not hope anymore
This is me
Alone.

Annie Cunningham

YOUR INTENTIONS?

The very first night we met,
Which is very unlike me,
We entwined together as one
Through passion and ecstasy.

Content with casual sex,
I soon went on my way,
That cold and frosty morning,
Off to work I went that day.

On occasions we would meet,
You were so caring, kind and true,
Speaking from your open heart
Is this person really you?

You said the most beautiful things,
I couldn't believe my luck,
A tall and handsome gentleman,
Could even take a look.

These nights we spent together,
You held me so close and dear,
We'd sit and drink and talk a lot,
I've never felt so near.

Not long before the tables turned,
All happened so very fast,
No longer content with casual sex,
It seems a spell you've cast!

But as I opened up my arms,
To comfort you right back,
You turned quick into something else
So heartless, cold and black!

Jenna Anne Clemance

GHOST SHIP

She moves alone through darkness, the mist her cloak of awe,
she would freeze the hardened sailor who would dare to step aboard.
All through the night she wanders, alone and far from shore,
the rigging drips of purple blood, by death with gun and sword.

No crew has she to speak of, the decks they hark and creek,
no moon could blaze her windswept ways, out through the mist
                                                    she peeps.
The sharks that follow slowly, black eyes above the wake,
be careful ye may flounder, your life she may just take.

The black flag on her main sail, stands strong and cannot yield,
her journey ever onward, her haunted broken keel.
Her cannons roll so slowly, back and forth just like the tides,
be careful ye unspoilt youth, they can burn and melt young eyes.

Never gaze at night, poor soulful youth, from the cliff tops
                                          strengthened heights,
for just beyond the horizon, there she drifts with mournful plight,
take care in case she beckons forth, her treasure you may seek,
beneath the waves she'll drag you, a salty grave you'll keep.

Out in the night she travels, for her no thought of shore,
for she is cursed and afflicted, to sail on for evermore.
I tell this tale to you my friend, I am the master of this craft,
through seven seas of gales and breeze, for the ghost ship,
                                          she's my heart.

Fergus Condron

TRUE LOVE LOST AGAIN IN FOGGY NOVEMBER YEAR ROUND

We met in October I always remember
Parted, got lost in foggy November
Met again by chance at a party in December
To celebrate the new year we kissed and cuddled
She sent me a hand painted Valentine card with guess who?
We were blown away again by the winds and march of time too
Darling I was such a fool so confused and muddled
Sweetheart you were so wise and our love blossomed like the
                                                    buds in May
Our joy came from within, we were happy and gay
Love prevailed you had your way
Soon you were to become my bride in June
In weeks we set up home not to be alone or on our own
Then came the summer months and holiday
Followed I remember by that sad September
The day, the hour, the minute you died
I burst into tears and cried and cried
I miss you darling so very, very much
All of me and my very soul you did touch
Because of me it took so long to come together
Your words still comfort me all the year round, all weathers
They were so sound, so profound, so true I thank you
You said, dear don't feel guilty about anything
In summer, autumn, winter or spring
You took so long to come yet you were the light of life you shone
Sadly now so quickly gone.

Allan John Mepstone

LOVE'S COLD HAND

You will sleep with my ghost tonight lover,
You murdered my soul with your regret,
And I will torment your dreams
with my voice and face,
Ever calling your name,
Even in the wind in the trees,
The spirit of the sea,
And the rap of the rain on
the window's pane.
My heart will chase yours
to the world's end
while my voice lilts honeyed nothings
and my face passively smiles,
But when I catch you,
Put my loving hand on your running shoulder,
You will turn around,
And with a final twist of your heedless knife,
Plunge me deep into insanity's waters,
And I will utter myriad of silent screams
as chained, you bring me to my knees
to pray for feet that run
away from you and love's cold hand.

Becky Cherri

THE JILTED MAN

You've broken up
and your wife has gone,
your marriage is dead,
but life goes on.

You're thirty something
and still looking good,
hold your head up high
and be strong dude.

You're going to get depressed
and turn to drink,
but it's better to get laid,
well at least that's what I think.

So remember you're free,
to have a woman or two,
it will make you feel better,
feeling someone next to you.

Because that's what you're used to
and that's what you need
and now you have a second chance,
to go and sow your seed.

A chapter of your life has gone,
but there will be plenty more,
no one knows,
what life has in store.

So put the past aside
and make the most of every new day,
it's your life,
so live it your way.

Stanley Bruce

THE LOVE BETWEEN TWO WORLDS

The love between two worlds,
Minds linked within our dreams,
Oh my dearest, by each passing hour,
Our love unfurls like an exotic flower.
Reaching out briefly, lightly touching,
Across the cosmic streams,
Passed silent suns we hurl,
Through the great galactic wheel,
Until in our comforting slumber,
Meeting again, my love, face to face.
We are angels of space's deep night,
Two linked souls in heavenly flight,
Lovers linked through time and space.
For our love knows no bounds,
Reaching out, our souls united,
Like the stand's a boundary,
The border between sea and land
We standing together on Holy ground,
Not on our separate Earth's,
Far from the planets of our birth,
But by some enchantment found.
A united love, amongst the stars,
Shining forth, a pulsating pearl,
As a perfect rose our souls unfurl,
So blossoms the love between two worlds.

Julia Pegg

FOREVER

'Forever' is a great hyperbole,
Three years is all it was for you and me.
Three years and then you cruelly turned your back,
Three years and then you gave my love the sack.
I thought 'forever' meant just what it said,
It seems, though, it's a word I have misread.
In apathetic tones you said goodbye,
You only get 'forever' when you die.

'Forever' is a great hyperbole,
Three years is all it was for love and me.
Three years until at last I saw
One closed but many open doors.
No two alike but each one meant the same:
Each one a chance at what I'd lost again.
In apathetic tones you called goodbye,
While fading like an image from the corner of my eye.

Chris Scriven

MY LITTLE BOY, MY LITTLE GIRL

My little girl and my little boy:
Now grown up and gone away.
My little boy with whom I sang
'Popeye the Sailor Man', and
A host of other silly songs,
Such happy silly songs;
And my little girl who,
Sang in the choir at school
And played the trumpet too.
Who put trusting hand in mine,
Looking up at me
And at the world with eyes
Full of wonder and of awe.
Who asked, 'Grandad what?'
And, 'Grandad, why?'
They wanted to know the answers,
Now they know them all.
And want to be pop stars,
Or have boyfriends and girlfriends.
Quite natural of course,
In the present run of things.
But my hand grasps empty air,
And I sit at home, alone.
No stories to make up,
Wracking brain for something new to tell.
No walks to explore,
The fields and woods.
Nor urban shops to gaze before,
Counting pennies.
I still count pennies,
But they are my own.
My little girl, my little boy.
My little boy, my little girl.
Children and grandchildren,
Now gone.

Roger Penney

YOUNG LOVE

I'm sorry I don't know what you want me to say
I'm sorry but my patience has all blown away
I'm sorry that I left you with tears on your face
I'm sorry that you think I'm a f*****g disgrace!

So what if I don't need you like you say you need me
I have to get out, be happy and free
You tell me I'm a loser, a worthless freak
Well get over yourself cos you're no better than me!

Lewis Haley

GREATEST DAY OF MY LIFE . . . BEING LOVERS

I'll put the kettle on.
I felt a flush spread all over my body.
He came over and, looking deep into my eyes,
He took my hand and kissed it.
By now I was trembling so much I *was spilling my tea.*
I had to sit down. My eyes closed up.
They started taking. So close together.
I didn't have a clue what they were talking about.
Minutes later he was off and I said to my friend:
'You didn't tell me your dad was so good looking.'
She said, 'Watch yourself.
He's a lady-killer, since his wife died a few years ago.
Thinks he's God's gift to women now.'
There was only one problem . . . I was 16 and he was 60.
I didn't care within my heart.
I *took him some oatcakes* . . . to the bathroom.
And I knocked on the door, and my knees were shaking.
When he opened it he said: ''Oh, it's you.'
He was standing there naked except for a towel round his middle.
He said, 'Come on in my dear.
I was just having a shower, put the cakes on the table.'
An hour later we were still chatting.
'I like your motorbike,' I said to him.
'Come on then,' replied Bob, 'I'll take you for a spin.'
I wrapped my arms tightly round his waist and rested my head
                                        on his shoulders.

After that became a regular visitor to Bob's house with his daughter,
We're such good friends together.
Months later, we discover we had lots in common.
I shall be here daily, I Sonnia, had more fun with him than with any of
My friends of my own age.
Then we sat by the fire with a glass of wine and talked again.
We made a pact that we would be together for the rest of our lives,
Enjoying one another's company.
Two years later, we were still together and in love.

A few months on, a small package here he said, 'Open it.'
I did so. A gold and sapphire cluster engagement ring.
Still together after 10 years, 3 lovely children.
People will always gossip and talk, but we take no notice.
His daughter got married too, with an older man too.

Viv Lionel Borer

LAST DANCE

Heard a song
down at the club
it mixes well
with most of the children of hell
but reminded me
of the wife and me
it kept on my mind
save the last dance for me
oh yeah save the last dance for me
oh babe save, save the last dance for me

Memories flood till when I'm in love
memories make me cry
when she told me she had to fly
when she told me
oh babe! when she told me
oh babe! when she told me she had to fly

I know I believed it at the time
me and my girl
would never falter, never shine
me and my girl
but she went away
but the worst, she never took
her love away
so am hurting
hurting inside
all I am now is
oh babe! a broken-down mind
oh babe! a broken-down mind

Paul Davidson

To My Love

I want to take you to my heart;
    wrap my arms around your soul;
with the softest brush of my lips,
    caress its form and every corner of your mind
until you are wrapped in a tenderness
    you have never before known.

I want to take you by the hand
    and dance with you on clouds;
place stars in your hair and wish
    upon every one the fulfilment
of your tender heart's
    most deepest longing.

I want to gaze into the beauty of your eyes
    and find again the deepest depth of you;
through softest eyes, to know and touch and hold you;
    and, lying in the depths of your soul,
to feel we cannot part.

I want to caress every portion of your being,
    to cover you with happiness;
to wrap your life in magic
    and take you to the New Dawn where
together, we will watch the sunrise
    and, in softness's tender depths,
I will press my lips to yours
    in one eternal kiss.

Christala Rosina

THOSE EYES

Some say careers are made from
        eyes
those eyes:
magazine covers
station clocks
living with the
pigeon s**t

watching.

rhythms s
        w
            a
                g g e r
                    in
                        the
                            world
green pools
                shimmer . . .

we skim stones to
break the ice
the ice doesn't give

faces change
        but not
        those eyes
although sometimes stained
by passers-by
with dirt from the snow
and vomit
from the evening show

just now
in *your* eyes I see
Moses with stones and fire

Great depths
into cauldrons
through the smallest arrow slits
- you too could go far with
t h o s e e y e s

welding perhaps?

Ian Bishop

STRANGE LOVE

Take me along with you!
I can't wait with eyes shut,
I'll go where you want me to,
Where you are my love!
I'll be there with you,
I'll be happy with you
From morning to night.
In the heat of moment,
On the verge of tears,
In the shade of the horizon,
In the depth of winter and the summer,
In the worse and the better.
I miss you, I'm thinking of you,
Take me along with you.
For my college years, much to regret,
In my loneliness, for my illness and sadness
For that old flame!
With my school maam,
For that innocent love
Washed away by the tide,
Buffeted by the waves,
For my heart crushed by grief
Take me along with you,
In the middle of war and the peace,
High up on the air, why not in the space!
In every nook and cranny,
In the sun-scorched earth,
Near you honey, be an earthly paradise.

Hacene Rahmouni

PARADISE AND THE BEACH IS A PERFECT WIFE

Woken up
Look out the window
There's a grey crane on the grass
Standing so still like a pane of glass
I watch for a minute, pretend I'm not there
Suddenly it turns to me, nervously it stares
Pulls out its great wings
Flying away it's a scary bird thing.

Get up out of bed
Time to get fed
Shower and away I go
Busy day ahead.

Get into my jeep I drive a few miles
To the beach, people are happy or getting high
Drink and relax for a while
The beach is never too many miles when you're feeling high
Met some friends, talked 'bout what to do tonight
Maybe stay out of town, stay out of the lights
Where can you go when you've got it all . . . ?
Going on in your perfect world
So many people friends for life
Paradise and the beach is a perfect wife.

Stephen A Owen

PURPLE PLEASURE

Why is your heart
a heart of leather?
Reassure me
with purple pleasure.

Your breasts
so hungry
while I'm bleeding
while I'm feeding.

Kiss my strawberry sunset
swallow my soul
I pluck your feathers
with purple pleasure.

Inside you
I will find you,
we tango in the heather
your lips devouring
my purple pleasure.

Craig Shuttleworth

THE KISS

I kissed his photograph today
My finger with moist love carried on trembling tip
Caressed the glass and lingered
Thoughts were urged across unknown ethers
Memories forged a patchwork path
And left my earthly body lonely and afraid

I kissed his photograph today
And relived the magic of closeness
Sunlight on hair - burnished and precious
The smell of earth and skin

I kissed his photograph today
Knowing that to want too much
Surely closes all doors
Keeps unearthly beings at bay

But still I kissed his photograph today
And the cut of sweet morning air
Brushed against my cheek

Anna Shannon

COMFORT

The past you say is dead
Live for today not yesterday
The days of the week are the same
The cloud and the cold have come again
As I walk these streets alone
Strange it is but I'm not alone
A faint whiff of you remains
Only on these particular days
Conversations come alive
Remembering words that have died
Smiles, frowns and laughter
Promise a heaven hereafter.

Raymond P G Rapson

UNTITLED

As empty as the eyes
of one who drinks alone.

Yet filled with dark broken shards
of angry flint sharp stone.

Absorbing the salt of sorrows fallen
that quickly dries on sun-bleached bone.

Swelling slowly with sad regret
as it reaps all that it has sown.

A broken clock keeping broken time
empty hands on a face of stone.

My heart is empty as the eyes
of one who drinks alone.

Peter Wilson

IT'S NEVER TOO LATE

They often say love is blind,
In my case never,
A truer word was said,
I ignored what was racing through my head.

She and I were childhood sweethearts,
But maturity and peer pressure,
Had put some distance between us,
Although we still lived next door to each other,
Between us you could drive a bus.

Romance with others for us both came and went,
Pledges and promises rose and floundered,
We were always it seemed pushed back together,
At one we were not, but apart never.

Then one day years down the line, her dear father died,
As good neighbours and friends we rallied round,
I helped her sort out, what needed sorting, in her corner I stood,
Quite unexpectedly I saw her in a far different light,
And suddenly I understood.

Realising what a fool I'd been,
Searching far and wide for what was on my doorstep,
Too blinkered, too blind to see,
The beauty and charm that was there in front of me.

At first she was suspicious of my intentions,
Thinking I was just being kind because of her loss,
She was confused, ignored my advances,
Saying we've been here before, pouring cold water on my chances.

Then she had a hot date, with some dashing man,
My boats were burned, my bridges crossed,
On her list, I was least and last,
I was as she said, part of her past.

Next day I saw her at the gate, asked her how had she enjoyed her date,
She said it was a disaster, a sham, she put her head on my shoulder,
And whispered for us perhaps it's not too late.

P J Littlefield

ON THE DEATH OF MY HUSBAND

Damp, sweaty sheets, feverish brow,
Eyes stabbed by the light -
We'll use candlelight now.

I hold your hand gently,
I keep my voice low -
There's so much to say, love,
Before you let go.

We have much to remember
Down the years we have shared,
Children and laughter
And joy uncompared.

There's been sadness and sorrow,
Bur our love has been true -
We've faced problems together
And always won through.

And now you are drifting,
You've nothing to fear,
Your pain will soon vanish,
Angel wings hover near.

In the midst of his anguish,
I ask you, 'Lord, why?'

But ask not, who is dying, love,
I know that it is I.

Jane Finlayson

A Mortal Blow

I had a boyfriend, he was my life,
He always told me, I'd be his wife,
He told me lies, and he deceived me too,
So in the end, I said we're through.
I had him back loads of times,
Because I loved him, and he was mine,
He's supposed to love me, so he said,
But his feelings towards me, always felt dead,
He said he'd change a number of times.
I must be out of my tiny mind,
He treated me bad, he was so unkind,
He said he loved me, but wouldn't commit,
In the end, I'd had enough of it.
He can't be trusted, that's something else,
If I wait for him, I'll be left on the shelf.
So you see, it's all down to me,
To go and look, for someone else
That can love me, in the way I should be,
So when he whispers, those three words
And does everything for me, that he can,
I know I have a future
With another man.

Mary Woolvin

DREAMS

You come to me in my dreams,
When the dark shadows cloud my rest,
The ice cold feel of fear in me,
Lost in the mist of confusion.

You come to me in my dreams,
When the dark shadows cloud my rest,
Your love reaches out to me,
Thinning the mist of confusion.

You come to me in my dreams,
When the dark shadows cloud my rest,
Your safe, comforting arms hold me,
Banishing the mist of confusion.

You come to me in my dreams,
When the dark shadows cloud my rest,
Your velvet lips caress me,
What mist of confusion?

You come to me in my dreams,
When dark shadows clouded my rest,
Our gentle, tender love embraces me,
Led me through the mist of confusion.

Seawitch (Alison Wells)

WHAT DO YOU SEE?

What do your eyes see when they look at me?
They see an adoring suitor yearning
For you to feel the heat of my burning
Heart and embrace my passion wildly.
They see tumultuously lustful fire,
The shock of desire shooting through my brain
In such a pleasurably violent pain
Singing songs of love like an angel's choir.

What do my eyes see when they look at you?
They see perfection in the human mould;
A resplendent beauty that takes a hold
Of anyone seeing this stunning view.
They see a girl whose smile can confiscate
My senses and do with them whatever
She may choose from this day and forever.
When my eyes look at you, they see my fate.

Clive E Oseman

FOR MY HUSBAND . . .

A moment in time to tell you,
that I love the man you are,
for even through the toughest of times,
you never went very far . . .
You've been there to see me smile,
to giggle and laugh with me,
to wipe away my tears,
to know when to let me be . . .
You've always tried to see me through,
the reaching of my dreams,
even when it seemed like,
our life was coming apart at the seams . . .
We've danced a million dances,
and held each other tight,
we've learned how to say 'I'm sorry',
and go on to make things right . . .
We've laid out in the grass,
and counted stars in the sky,
believing in our destiny,
not always questioning why . . .
In these years we've had together,
we've seen trials of our love,
we've passed with flying colours,
and the graces from above . . .
I smile when I think ahead,
to growing old, with you in my life,
knowing that we'll live our days,
always, man and wife.

Kitty Morgan

A MOMENT

If in every moment of my life,
a dream of mine had been fulfilled.
Not all of those moments together
would compare,
to one moment spent with you.

Sue Tobin

SOULMATE

And you stare back at me
From the glossy page,
Smile like a mischievous child's,
Shape still slender and boyish,
With your gentle blue eyes
And the bump in your nose.

It's not your fault that you can't
Hold for too long, heavy weights,
Or open the jars' too tight lids;
Your numb hands are always cold,
Condemned by the painful, icy tingle
Of Carpal tunnel syndrome.

You were persistent and kind - always there,
Always true
When I almost rejected you,
But you kept hanging on,
Too stubborn to leave me
To the fate I deserved,
For so long.

With your floppy brown hair
And your razor-like mind,
Brain racing like a comet,
Heart generous like rainfall,
You came into my life,
My small, sturdy oak,
Taking permanent root in
My heart.

Now I cannot imagine a day
Without you,
An hour, a minute, a second would be
Too long,
You've become my time, my purpose,
My pattern,
You are my heart, my hope -
My song.

Kay Jude

WHO ALWAYS LOVES YOU

Who to turn to
In moments of need
And nothing can please
Who do you turn to
When life has gone wrong
The moments you shared
Have all blown and gone
Who can you trust
When friends let you down
Your private thoughts scattered
All over the ground
Who always loves you
Whatever you do
Wherever you go
God will be there with you

Jeanette Gaffney

In The Name Of Love

Little children, little children
We watch over you
Bathe you, feed you
And protect -
All in the name of love.

Little children now no more
And we are old and grey
Will you remember then
And now protect -
All in the name of love?

Opal Innsbruk

As Long As There Is Love

You hurt me like hell
But still I forgive you
Because you say I mean the world.

Should I believe you?
Should I leave you?
Only time will tell.

You say you love me
And I'm inclined to believe you
As long as there is love I don't care.

One more time though
And you're out the door,
At least that's what I always say.

But if you love me
Just like you say
I'm sure it will be okay.

Nikki Rogers

LOOMING TORMENT

This torment's too strong,
as my emotions know it's wrong.
But nature's took control,
while life must go - on and on and on.

It's my deep need, to be loved,
and be comforted - longingly held.
Which drives my searching heart,
always to share - while passions blend.

With always feeling there's nothing for me,
no love to share or passions intertwined,
no! - Nothing out there.

My need's so deep,
so all consuming.
It's more diverse than greed,
yet will always be,
          - eternally looming.

Gary J Finlay

THINGS I LOVE ABOUT YOU

Your smile, your face, your voice, your thighs,
the back of your neck, your laugh and your eyes.

Your intelligence and the way you stay calm,
your back, your shoulders, your hands and your arms.

Your kindness, your logic, your incredible drive,
your passion (which brings me back to those thighs!)

Your strength, both physical and mental,
I have no doubts; you are very 'special'.

Gillian L Wise

BEST FRIEND AND LOVER

Poetry comes from what's in your head,
Without our memories we may as well be dead.
We should learn from our mistakes,
And do whatever it takes.

To better our lives and learn from the past,
And find a new love that will last.
Friendship must be first it is a must,
It's not always good to start off with lust.

Those feelings are great but they don't always last,
And then you'd be living another fast.
But to build a friendship honest and true,
You grow a stronger love between the two of you.

A love that will hold up when the going gets rough,
Love's not always easy it's sometimes tough.
If your lover is your lover and best friend rolled into one,
It makes it so much easier when the bad days come.

A shoulder to cry on if they really care,
When you need them they're always there.
Ready to lift you when you've fallen down,
To give you a smile to replace your frown.

To gently hold you and keep you warm,
Together you'd be able to weather the storm.
Together you'd be united, a bond so strong,
You'd be able to talk about it if something goes wrong.

Giving and receiving, sharing all,
Feeling this love will make you walk tall.
Look for a best friend before a lover,
You'll find the right one and won't need any other . . .

Angie Kesteven

TED

Another day done, the phones are quiet -
respite from the daily diet of stress.
I'm alone now, colleagues have left for home
leaving unwashed coffee cups among piles
of unfiled paperwork on groaning desks.
I glance out of the big, grimy window
facing north toward the busy A-road
and my mind is caught on the winds of time.
Long departed workmates enter the room
and a maelstrom of emotion strikes.
Old Ted urges me to give more time to
my loved ones. He's there, though invisible,
and his heart attack is re-enacted.
No panic, just a vision of a man
who was loved but all too rarely seen by
his wife and kids. We all considered Ted
indispensable. But life carried on
and the office continued to function.
Now it's me that is the most vital cog;
I share a coffee with Ted's memory,
head home to my neglected family,
and vow to prove my love, before I'm gone.

Clive E Oseman

SUBMISSIONS INVITED
SOMETHING FOR EVERYONE

POETRY NOW 2004 - Any subject,
any style, any time.

WOMENSWORDS 2004 - Strictly women,
have your say the female way!

STRONGWORDS 2004 - Warning!
Opinionated and have strong views.
(Not for the faint-hearted)

All poems no longer than 30 lines.
Always welcome! No fee!
Cash Prizes to be won!

Mark your envelope (eg *Poetry Now*) **2004**
Send to:
Forward Press Ltd
Remus House, Coltsfoot Drive,
Peterborough, PE2 9JX

OVER £10,000 POETRY PRIZES
TO BE WON!

Judging will take place in October 2004

CHAPTER ONE

EDITOR'S PICKS

The Secret Garden

EDITOR'S PICKS | FOR MORE INFO, SEE P80 |

As the name suggests, The Secret Garden, has just that - a beautiful walled garden to admire whilst enjoying brunch, afternoon tea, or an evening meal. The unique Pudding night - held once a month, has been created for those with a sweet tooth.

Woolpack Inn

EDITOR'S PICKS | FOR MORE INFO, SEE P41 |

The Woolpack Inn is an exceptional pub in the depths of Kent offering top notch pub grub, a friendly welcome as well as five beautiful and uniquely decorated rooms. Dishes include Fish Pie, Salt Marsh Beef Steak and Boozy Banana Split.

The Goods Shed

EDITOR'S PICKS | FOR MORE INFO, SEE P143

The Goods Shed is a daily farmers' market, providing the best from Kent's 'Garden of England'. The on-site restaurant with its open kitchen, serves distinctive dishes created from ingredients sourced from the market. Candlelit in the evening or suffused by sunlight the restaurant is full of ambience.

Saltwood on the Green

EDITOR'S PICKS | FOR MORE INFO, SEE P85

Saltwood on the Green focuses on simplicity and pristine ingredients, believing that if they do the hard work up-front by carefully choosing their suppliers and ingredients and work with the seasons, the dishes will create themselves.

Rocksalt

EDITOR'S PICKS | FOR MORE INFO, SEE P76 |

On a sunny afternoon, finer views are hard to find in Folkestone than those to be had from Rocksalt. This modern restaurant overlooks the busy little harbour and specialises in the day's catch by local fisherman wherever possible.

5

The Wife of Bath

PLACES TO EAT | FOR MORE INFO, SEE P88 |

The Wife of Bath is a highly regarded, contemporary restaurant serving Northern Spanish inspired dishes and is home to five beautiful en-suite bedrooms. A fusion of rustic and refined, the menu is innovative and utilises the best seasonal produce available, both locally and direct from Spain.

6

The Potting Shed

EDITOR'S PICKS | FOR MORE INFO, SEE P58 |

The Potting Shed is the latest addition from the team at Elite Pubs. This is the fifth of their ventures and a great addition to the family. The pub is unique in the choice of interior being decorated with gardening tools, urns and other agricultural based paraphernalia.

7

Windy Corner Stores

EDITOR'S PICKS | FOR MORE INFO, SEE P107

Windy Corner Stores in Whitstable is an understated café/restaurant that prides itself on selling the best of Kent's produce. The Guardian voted it one of the top ten budget restaurants on the North Kent coast.

8

The Beaney House

EDITOR'S PICKS | FOR MORE INFO, SEE P17

The Beaney House of Art and Knowledge is the central museum, library and art gallery of Canterbury. Housed in a Grade II listed building, this award winning facility provides state-of-the-art exhibition galleries, excellent educational facilities and a varied programme of events.

Broadstairs

EDITOR'S PICKS | FOR MORE INFO, SEE P12

The main attraction in Broadstairs is its magnificent horseshoe beach named Viking Bay. With its cliff top promenade and family activities, the area projects the essence of old-world seaside charm, with its colourful beach huts and anchored fishing boats.

Leeds Castle

EDITOR'S PICKS | FOR MORE INFO, SEE P16

Leeds Castle has been a Norman stronghold, the private property of six of England's medieval queens, a palace used by Henry VIII and his first wife Catherine of Aragon, a Jacobean country house, a Georgian mansion and an elegant early 20th century retreat for the influential and famous.

Hush Heath Vineyard

EDITOR'S PICKS | FOR MORE INFO, SEE P23

Hush Heath is a gorgeous, award winning vineyard based near Staplehurst in the Weald of Kent established by entrepreneur Richard Balfour-Lynn in 2010. You can visit seven days a week to take a self guided tour around their vineyards and apple orchards followed by a tutored tasting.

Deal

EDITOR'S PICKS | FOR MORE INFO, SEE P20 |

On a clear day you can see France on the horizon from the town of Deal which is situated just 25 miles from the mainland. Deal was formally a fishing, mining and garrison town and its position on the English Channel made it a significant and extremely busy port.

13

Dungeness

EDITOR'S PICKS | FOR MORE INFO, SEE P15 |

Dungeness is unique. This desolate landscape is home to wooden houses, a nuclear power station, lighthouses, a narrow gauge railway, nature and bird reserves, the RNLI, expansive gravel pits and the ruins of many boats and shacks.

14

Gusbourne Vineyard

EDITOR'S PICKS | FOR MORE INFO, SEE P22 |

Gusbourne is a stunning English wine estate made up of 61 hectares in Kent and a further 32 in West Sussex near to the Goodwood estate. The first vines were planted in 2004 by Andrew Weeber who saw the potential of the existing farm land and the Kent climate.

15

The Beacon

EDITOR'S PICKS | FOR MORE INFO, SEE P78 |

The Beacon is a stylish, contemporary restaurant with mesmerising views over the valley and onwards to Tunbridge Wells. Open, roaring fires, rustic furnishings and flickering candles make the space cozy and welcoming. They have kept their menu simple, with great attention to the quality of the ingredients.

16

Turner Contemporary

EDITOR'S PICKS | **FOR MORE INFO, SEE P16**

Turner Contemporary is one of the UK's leading a galleries, offering diverse exhibitions of contempora and historical art. The Turner Contemporary has fre admission and is located directly on the seafront, the site where Turner would stay when visiting t town.

The Farm House

EDITOR'S PICKS | **FOR MORE INFO, SEE P61**

The Farm House, another member of the successf Elite Pub family, is a village pub set within an Elizabeth House and situated in the heart of the old market tov of West Malling, a historic market town North East Royal Tunbridge Wells.

The Sportsman

EDITOR'S PICKS | **FOR MORE INFO, SEE P46**

The Sportsman in Seasalter is an unlikely spot for gastronomic delight but their reputation for fres quality fish is superb. The kitchen is run by Steph Harris who has earned a Michelin star whilst cookir here. Stephen sources many quality ingredients fro the local Monks Hill Farm.

Whitstable

EDITOR'S PICKS | **FOR MORE INFO, SEE P10**

Whitstable is renowned for its culinary excellence a pretty seaside charm. This seaside retreat is popul due to its sophisticated and contemporary approa to food and its attractive aesthetic. The town has be celebrated for its seafood since Roman times.

CHAPTER SEVEN

OUT &
ABOUT

Whitstable

OUT & ABOUT | WHITSTABLE | CT5 1AJ

Whitstable is renowned for its culinary excellence and pretty seaside charm. This seaside retreat is popular due to its sophisticated and contemporary approach to food and its attractive aesthetic. The town has been celebrated for its seafood since Roman times.

Situated on the North East Kent coast, Whitstable is close to the city of Canterbury and has a strong art culture. The harbour has a popular fish market, with the daily catch showcased on ice. Its multitude of excellent eateries from Wheelers to The Sportsman are regularly featured in the national media.

ADDRESS

34, Harbour Street, Whitstable CT5 1AJ

PHONE

01227 770060

NEAR HERE

The Old Neptune (p39)

Wheelers Oyster Bar (p83)

Windy Corner Stores (p107)

Kingsgate and Botany Bay

OUT & ABOUT | **BOTANY BAY** | CT10 3LG

Kingsgate and Botany Bay are fantastic sandy coves located just out of Broadstairs and Margate. Natural arches, white cliffs and deep caves, make this a natural, hidden corner. The clean, clear waters are great for swimming and the rock pools and possible fossil finds can keep families busy for hours.

The ends of both beaches get cut off at high tide and Botany Bay, like many popular beaches, has a dog ban in place from the 1st May until 30th September between 10am and 6pm when the beach is at its busiest.

ADDRESS

Marine Drive, Kingsgate
CT10 3LG

PHONE

01843 577577

NEAR HERE

Turner Contemporary (p169)

Margate Beach (p33)

Sandwich and Pegwell Bay (p33)

Broadstairs

OUT & ABOUT | BROADSTAIRS | CT10 1LZ

The main attraction in Broadstairs is its magnificent horseshoe beach named Viking Bay. With its cliff top promenade and family activities, the area projects the essence of old-world seaside charm, with its colourful beach huts and anchored fishing boats.

Broadstairs was reportedly Charles Dickens' favourite holiday destination and Bleak House, the cliff top house in which he stayed in the 1850s and 1860s, can be visited. Broadchurch offers various activities for families throughout the year from its Dickens Festival to its surfing schools and food festival.

ADDRESS
The Parade, Broadstairs
CT10 1LZ

PHONE
N/A

NEAR HERE
Wyatt and Jones (p92)
The Falstaff (p54)
Royal Harbour Brasserie (p89)

Canterbury

Situated on the river Stour, the historic cathedral city of Canterbury is a UNESCO world heritage site. Occupied since Palaeolithic times, many historic architectural structures populate the area, including its landmark cathedral, the Roman city wall, a Norman castle and the ruins of St Augustine's Abbey.

Canterbury is a scenic town with highly regarded eateries scattered amongst the medieval streets and along the riverside. As one of England's most popular tourist destination cities, the ambience is cosmopolitan and a hive of activity from its universities and festivals to its popular theatre scene.

ADDRESS

18 High Street, Canterbury
CT1 2RA

PHONE

01227 862162

NEAR HERE

The Goods Shed (p143)

Refectory Kitchen (p94)

Waterlane Coffeehouse (p106)

Tonbridge

OUT & ABOUT | **TONBRIDGE** | **TN9 1BG**

The market town of Tonbridge is less than 30 miles South East of London where Georgian manor houses and a hill top, 11th century castle await. The walkway alongside the river has recently been renovated and the high street is characterful with a number of independant retailers.

Keep an eye out for the regular Farmer's Markets and food fairs which are held in the centre of town. The recently restored Hadlow Tower in the nearby Medway valley is also worth a visit.

ADDRESS
Castle Street, Tonbridge
TN9 1BG

PHONE
01732 770929

NEAR HERE
The Old Firestation (p104)
The Twenty Six (p77)
The Poet (p50)

Dungeness

OUT & ABOUT | DUNGENESS | TN29 9NE

Dungeness is unique. This desolate landscape is home to wooden houses, a nuclear power station, lighthouses, a narrow gauge railway, nature and bird reserves, the RNLI, expansive gravel pits and the ruins of many boats and shacks.

It possesses a rich and diverse wildlife within the National Nature Reserve in one of the largest shingle landscapes in the world and had been used in countless films and music videos. A selection of pubs specialising in local fish and a traditional fish smokery also form part of the local attractions.

ADDRESS

Dungeness Rd
TN29 9NE

PHONE

N/A

NEAR HERE

RH & D Railway (p29)

Mary's Tea Room (p130)

Folkestone Harbour (p21)

Margate

OUT & ABOUT | MARGATE | CT9 1JD

Margate's internationally acclaimed Turner Contemporary gallery, showcasing contemporary and historical art works has put Margate back on the map. Previously known as a seaside holiday destination, the area is fast becoming an artistic centre with families also returning to its beaches after a period of regeneration.

Margate's old town is becoming renowned for its contemporary eateries and as a vintage shopping destination juxtaposed against its traditional seaside attractions, from seafood stalls to retro ice cream shops.

ADDRESS

Droit House, Stone Pier, Margate
CT9 1JD

PHONE

01843 577577

NEAR HERE

Turner Contemporary (p169)

GB Pizza Co (p82)

Margate Beach (p33)

Royal Tunbridge Wells

OUT & ABOUT | **TUNBRIDGE WELLS** | **TN2 5TE**

Named after the natural spring which welled up from the ground over 400 years ago, the spa town of Tunbridge Wells quickly became associated with royalty and adopted 'royal' into its title, when Queen Victoria made it her regular holiday destination. The town is surrounded by the beautiful scenery of the Garden of England.

Tunbridge Wells has a multitude of independant boutiques, chic hotels and popular cafes and restaurants. The colonnaded Georgian Pantiles area of the town is renowned for its charming tearooms, farmers market and a bandstand which often hosts jazz musicians during the Summer months.

ADDRESS

The Corn Exchange, The Pantiles, Tunbridge Wells TN2 5TE

PHONE

01892 515675

NEAR HERE

The Bicycle Bakery (p155)

The Cake Shed (p119)

The Beacon (p78)

Rochester

OUT & ABOUT | ROCHESTER | ME1 1LX

Rochester's Norman castle and ancient cathedral situated above the Medway river, make it a scenic city to visit. Its winding cobbled streets, flint walls and scenic views are steeped in history. Charles Dickens grew up in this region in neighbouring Chatham and many of his greatest works were written here.

Rochester's strategic importance near the confluence of the river Thames and The Medway, led to the construction of Rochester Castle, built to guard the river crossing. Its Norman tower-keep of Kentish ragstone was built around 1127 and the castle remained as a viable fortress until the sixteenth century.

ADDRESS

95 High Street, Rochester
ME1 1LX

PHONE

01634 338141

NEAR HERE

Rochester Castle (p175)

Olivers (p98)

The Seaplane Works (p131)

Sandwich

Sandwich is situated on the River Stour. This small medieval town and its historic centre have been well preserved and Sandwich Bay, a sweeping inlet of sea, is considered an area of high ecological importance, with areas of conservation and bird protection. The town is where the bread snack originated.

Sandwich is one of the Cinque Port Towns, formed for trade and military purposes from around the 11th century however due to the disappearance of the Wantsum Channel, it is now approximately two miles from the sea. The surrounding area is believed to be the landing place for the Roman invasion of Britain in AD43.

Guildhall, Cattle Market,
Sandwich
CT13 9AH

01304 613565

George and the Dragon (p65)

The Salutation Gardens (p32)

Sandwich Harbour (p33)

Deal

OUT & ABOUT | **DEAL** | CT14 6TR

On a clear day you can see France on the horizon from the town of Deal which is situated just 25 miles from the mainland. Deal was formally a fishing, mining and garrison town and its position on the English Channel made it a significant and extremely busy port.

Today, Deal is a seaside resort with charming Georgian architecture and a wide stretch of beach. Deal's winding, pedestrianised high street is lined with an array of innovative independant cafes and restaurants. Its Tudor castle, built to prevent French invasion, has a fascinating history.

ADDRESS
Town Hall, High Street, Deal
CT14 6TR

PHONE
01304 369576

NEAR HERE
Deal Castle (p171)
Popup Cafe (p120)
The Freed Man (p52)

Folkestone Harbour

lkestone Harbour has recently undergone dramatic changes and e remainder of the seafront is currently being developed as part the town's regeneration process. The history of the harbour is tensive with King Henry having made a visit back in 1542 before s planned war against France.

e Harbour makes a good spot for a stroll along the waters edge see what the local fishermen have caught that morning. A short alk further and you will come across the popular Sunny Sands each. Expect big change in this part of England as 1,000 homes d 10,000 sq m of retail space are planned in the near future.

ADDRESS

The Stade
CT19 6AB

PHONE

01303 254597

NEAR HERE

Lower Leas Coastal Park (p33)
Royal Military Canal (p34)
The Secret Garden (p80)

Gusbourne Vineyard

OUT & ABOUT | APPLEDORE | TN26 2BE

Gusbourne is a stunning English wine estate made up of 61 hectares in Kent and a further 32 in West Sussex near to the Goodwood estate. The first vines were planted in 2004 by Andrew Weeber who saw the potential of the existing farm land and the Kent climate.

All wine is made from their own harvest and the grapes planted are made up of the classic varieties of Chardonnay, Pinot Noir and Pinot Meunier. They have recently been awarded two Platinum Gold Medals at the Decanter World Wine Awards 2016.

ADDRESS

Kenardington Road
TN26 2BE

PHONE

01233 758 666

NEAR HERE

Woolpack Inn (p41)

Chapel Down Vineyard (p25)

RH & D Railway (p29)

Hush Heath Vineyard

OUT & ABOUT | STAPLEHURST | TN12 0HT

Hush Heath is a gorgeous, award winning vineyard based near Staplehurst in the Weald of Kent, established by entrepreneur Richard Balfour-Lynn in 2010. You can visit seven days a week to take a self guided tour around their vineyards and apple orchards followed by a tutored tasting without charge. They're open 11am to 4pm.

They use traditional Champagne methods combined with an emphasis on biodiversity and natural techniques to create a range of wines and cider. Combined with a visit to their sister pub, The Goudhurst Inn, we think this is a pretty special day out.

ADDRESS
Five Oak Lane
TN12 0HT

PHONE
01622 832 794

NEAR HERE
Frankies Farmshop (p148)
The Mulberry Tree (p99)
Biddenden Vineyard (p24)

Biddenden Vineyard

OUT & ABOUT | BIDDENDEN | TN27 8DF

Biddenden is an award winning, family run, 23 acre vineyard located near Tenterden in Kent that produce their own range of wine and cider. They are the oldest commercial vineyard in Kent having been established in 1969.

Admission and tastings are free and the vineyard is open to the public all year round. There is also a coffee shop on site to fulfil your cake and tea requirements. They are open 10-5 Monday to Friday and 11-5 on Sundays.

ADDRESS
Gribble Bridge Lane
TN27 8DF

PHONE
01580 291 726

NEAR HERE
Bloomsburys (p113)
The West House (p87)
Silcocks Farm Shop (p152)

Chapel Down Vineyard

OUT & ABOUT | TENTERDEN | TN30 7NG

Chapel Down in Tenterden is an established Kent based wine estate and home to England's leading winemaker. The estate produces a range of still and sparkling wines as well as their own beer and cider and enjoys 50,000 visitors per year.

The winery is open all year round from 10am-5pm and offers guided tours from March – November. They also have a modern British restaurant, herb garden and shop on site.

ADDRESS

Small Hythe Road
TN30 7NG

PHONE

01580 766 111

NEAR HERE

Gusbourne Vineyard (p22)

The Old Dairy Brewery (p31)

The Queen's Inn (p74)

Tonbridge Castle

OUT & ABOUT | TONBRIDGE | TN9 1BG

Tonbridge Castle is reputedly England's finest example of a Motte and Bailey Castle. Boasting a splendid 13th Century Gatehouse, it is also surrounded by acres of beautiful grounds. An audio tour brings to life the rich history. Today the castle hosts open-air cinema and theatre nights during the summer.

When William the Conqueror came to England in 1066, the easily-built fortresses were the answer to protecting himself and his men against a potentially hostile population. Norman lords were put in charge of the construction of castles; Tonbridge was entrusted to Richard de Clare.

ADDRESS
Castle Street
TN9 1BG

PHONE
01732 770929

NEAR HERE
Tonbridge Canal (p34)
The Bakehouse at 124 (p128)
The Twenty Six (p77)

RH & D Railway

OUT & ABOUT | NEW ROMNEY | TN28 8PL

The miniature steam and diesel locomotives have powered their way along the 13½ miles of track of the Romney, Hythe and Dymchurch Railway for the past 88 years. There are 4 stations in between Hythe and Dungeness (a National Nature Reserve with one of the largest shingle landscapes in the world).

This railway gives you the opportunity to explore the beaches, lighthouses, wildlife and flora of this unique corner of Kent. New Romney Station in particular provides plenty to do, with the 1940's museum, play park and gift shop, perfect in any weather and for all generations.

ADDRESS

Littlestone Road
TN28 8PL

PHONE

01797 362353

NEAR HERE

Dungeness (p15)

Gusbourne Vineyard (p22)

Chapel Down Vineyard (p25)

Union Mill

OUT & ABOUT | CRANBROOK | TN17 3AH

Union Mill is a Grade I Listed mill in Cranbrook, Kent, which has been restored to working order and is the tallest smock mill in the United Kingdom. Flour milled on site and using only power from the wind can be purchased when you visit.

It was built in 1814 and restored in 1950. It is only open inside to visitors in the summer months however its charming aesthetic and structure make it interesting to view all year round. Entry is free but donations are welcomed.

ADDRESS

Russell's Road
TN17 3AH

PHONE

01580 891821

NEAR HERE

Biddenden Vineyard (p24)

Hush Heath Vineyard (p23)

The Milk House (p53)

Shepherd Neame Brewery

OUT & ABOUT | FAVERSHAM | ME13 7AX

Britain's oldest brewer offers a fascinating insight into the production of beer, from their rich heritage to the latest innovations. You can discover everything about the art of brewing, be it the well that supplies their 'liquor', traditional barrel-making, or their 21st century bottling techniques.

Shepherd Neame Brewery have repeatedly pioneered sustainable brewing methods to the benefit of the environment, the community and their future. They are proud to be the first UK brewery to attain full accreditation for the environmental management standard ISO 14001.

ADDRESS

17 Court Street
ME13 7AX

PHONE

01795 542016

Old Dairy Brewery

OUT & ABOUT | TENTERDEN | TN30 6HE

The Old Dairy Brewery began in 2010, when the brewery was set up in an old milking parlour in the Kent countryside. It was an immediate success, building a loyal fan base among ale enthusiasts who appreciated their finely crafted recipes, locally sourced ingredients and interesting variety of beer styles.

Thr brewery outgrew the milking parlour and in mid 2014, built a new one inside two World War II Nissen buildings in Tenterden, Kent (known as the 'jewel in the weald'). The brewery enjoys glorious views over the rolling hills and they also have a popular shop where you can buy their delicious beers.

ADDRESS

Station Road
TN30 6HE

PHONE

01580 763867

Dane John Gardens

OUT & ABOUT | CANTERBURY | CT1 1YW

Dane John Gardens offers excellent views over the city and the surrounding countryside from the top of the mound. Within the gardens is a safe play area for children, a fountain and a newly built bandstand which acts as a venue for traditional concerts throughout the summer.

Hythe Beach

OUT & ABOUT | HYTHE | CT21 6AW

If you're visiting the small coastal market town of Hythe, the pebble beach runs adjacent to the High Street and is an excellent place to stretch the legs along the Victorian seafront promenade. Hythe was once a bustling harbour and the central Cinque Port.

Westgate Gardens

OUT & ABOUT | CANTERBURY | CT1 2BQ

Westgate Parks are four distinctly different landscape character areas. Together they form a delightful stretch of recreational land which follows the Great Stour river from the heart of Canterbury's busy city centre into the countryside.

The Salutation Gardens

OUT & ABOUT | SANDWICH | CT13 9EW

By the river Stour in Sandwich, hidden behind the ancient town walls is the glorious Salutation Gardens. Three and a half acres of impressive grounds, perfect for strolling year round and a great space to relax in and appreciate the dynamic combination of old and new.

Sandwich Harbour

OUT & ABOUT | SANDWICH | CT13 9LY

Sandwich Harbour and the River Stour are both great spots for stretching the legs and immersing yourself in the local wildlife. Riverboats line the banks on either side and terns and gulls busy the shores.

Margate Beach

OUT & ABOUT | MARGATE | CT9 1XP

Margate beach is a wide expanse of sand with a certificate from Blue Flag to highlight the cleanliness of the water. The beach has good facilities for visitors. The traditional seaside town serves as a backdrop, with the world-class Turner Contemporary Gallery situated just a stone's throw away.

Sandwich and Pegwell Bay

OUT & ABOUT | SANDWICH | CT12 5JB

With an abundance of wildlife, especially birds, Sandwich and Pegwell Bay are great spaces for nature-lovers and families. It is Kent Wildlife Trust's largest nature reserve and is of international importance for its waders and wildfowl, best seen over winter or during the spring and autumn migrations.

Lower Leas Coastal Park

OUT & ABOUT | FOLKESTONE | CT20 2JP

The Lower Leas Coastal Park is positioned between Folkestone and Sandgate and has been developed into an award-winning recreational park having been awarded a Green Flag every year since 2007. The park is split into three areas, The Wild Zone, The Fun Zone and The Formal Zone.

Knole Park

OUT & ABOUT | SEVENOAKS | TN15 0RP

Nestled in a medieval deer-park, Knole is vast, complex and full of hidden treasures. Originally an Archbishop's palace, the house passed through royal hands to the Sackville family. Inside, art lovers can admire the works of Reynolds, Gainsborough and Van Dyck.

Tonbridge Canal

OUT & ABOUT | TONBRIDGE | TN9 1DR

Make like Ratty and Mole in 'Wind in the Willows' and enjoy messing about on the river. The area around Tonbridge is rich in history, has areas of natural beauty, acres of natural wildlife and are all connected by an unspoilt river: the River Medway (Tonbridge Northern Route).

Dover Beach

OUT & ABOUT | DOVER | CT16 1LQ

Dover harbour beach has the best seats in town for spotting the cross-channel ferries and is also a great spot for water-based activities including kayaking, canoeing, sailing and windsurfing. The beach is shingle, ideal for a spot of stone-skimming.

Royal Military Canal

OUT & ABOUT | HYTHE | CT21 6AX

The Royal Military Canal is 28 miles long, running from Seabrook in Kent to Cliff End in East Sussex. It is the third longest defensive monument in the British Isles after Hadrian's Wall and Offa's Dyke.

Notes

Tried our app?

bestofengland.com/app

CHAPTER TWO

PUBLIC HOUSES

The Old Neptune

PUBLIC HOUSES | WHITSTABLE | CT5 1EJ

The Old Neptune, known locally as Neppy, is a cozy, seaside boozer that is the subject of many a photo of Whitstable. The pub is located directly on the seafront which is an idyllic spot to spend an hour or two on a sunny afternoon.

They have a good selection of local ales and not so local lagers, as well as standard pub grub. They host live music events and are also dog friendly.

ADDRESS
Marine Terrace
CT5 1EJ

PHONE
01227 272262

NEAR HERE
David Brown Deli (p149)
The Sportsman (p46)
Frank (p141)

Duke of William

PUBLIC HOUSES | ICKHAM | CT3 1QP

Situated just ten minutes outside of the historic City of Canterbury, the Duke of William is a contemporary and stylish pub. With a roaring fire during the winter months, the idyllic garden is full of hanging baskets, potted plants, an olive tree and herb boxes during the summer.

The menu is built around the best local produce and suppliers the surrounding countryside and coastline has to offer. Seasonality is key, which is why their menus are constantly evolving. Guest rooms are softly decorated in Farrow and Ball shades, with vibrant pops of colour on contemporary furnishings.

ADDRESS

The Street
CT3 1QP

PHONE

01227 721308

NEAR HERE

Ye Olde Yew Tree Inn (p51)

Mama Feelgoods (p161)

The Goods Shed (p143)

Woolpack Inn

PUBLIC HOUSES | WAREHORNE | TN26 2LL

The Woolpack Inn is an exceptional pub in the depths of Kent offering top notch pub grub, a friendly welcome as well as five beautiful and uniquely decorated rooms. Dishes include Fish Pie, Salt Marsh Beef Steak and Boozy Banana Split.

This pub is the third of a family of nearby public houses, each of which has their own quirky style. Fires and wood burners are throughout, dogs are welcome and breakfast is served daily.

ADDRESS

Church Lane
TN26 2LL

PHONE

01233 732900

NEAR HERE

Gusbourne Vineyard (p22)

Mary's Tea Room (p130)

The Secret Garden (p80)

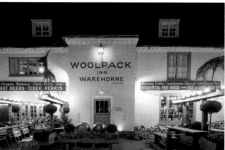

The Tickled Trout

PUBLIC HOUSES | WEST FARLEIGH | ME15 0PE

The Tickled Trout in West Farleigh is the second establishment owned by Kent winery, Hush Heath Estate who have given the pub a complete refit. Originally built in 1541, this Grade II listed building became an ale house in the mid 1700s and benefits from beamed ceilings and a zinc bar.

Dishes include fish pie and butternut squash and pumpkin ravioli. There are six boutique rooms which are accessed via their own private entrance. There's also an all important kids play area to keep the little ones entertained.

ADDRESS

Lower Road
ME15 0PE

PHONE

01622 814717

NEAR HERE

Leeds Castle (p164)

The Potting Shed (p58)

The Mulberry Tree (p99)

The Three Chimneys

PUBLIC HOUSES | BIDDENDEN | TN27 8LW

The Three Chimneys is an award winning independant country pub in Biddenden. The building dates back to 1420. Dark oak beams, a roaring fire and five separate dining areas make this a characterful and relaxed venue for a pint or a bite to eat.

Craig Smith, who packed in his City job to take over the pub in 1999 serves Welsh Rarebit, Haddock Fishcakes and deep fried brie. There are five luxury bedrooms available but oddly, only two chimneys. An ideal refreshment stop off if you are visiting Sissinghurst Castle or Scotney Castle. Dogs are welcome.

ADDRESS

Hareplain Road
TN27 8LW

PHONE

01580 291472

NEAR HERE

Bloomsburys (p113)

The Milk House (p53)

Biddenden Vineyard (p24)

The Pullman

PUBLIC HOUSES | FOLKESTONE | CT20 1SE

The Pullman in Folkestone is full of character and prides itself on serving "The best from the field and sea". This large pub has had an extensive refurbishment and is split into several rooms, with cosy fireplaces and soft candle lighting throughout.

Expect Kentish beef steaks, slow roast pork belly ribs and crispy fillet of bream with steamed clams. A visit to Folkestone would not be complete without a stop off at the Pullman.

ADDRESS

9 Church Street
CT20 1SE

PHONE

01303 488966

NEAR HERE

The Wing (p165)

The Café Collective (p114)

Folkestone Harbour (p21)

The Plough

PUBLIC HOUSES | LANGLEY | ME17 3LX

The Plough is a stylish gastro pub in the small country village of Langley. The new owners have employed 5* London chefs and a fully refurbished interior. Rich inky greys contrast against soft wood and leather furnishings and industrial metal pendant lights hang down from the bar.

The refurbishment contrasts industrial, masculine interior elements with the softer, traditional features of the pub such as the wooden beams. When we visited, scallops, mixed game terrine and grilled fillet steak were on the menu at this luxurious eatery.

ADDRESS

Sutton Road
ME17 3LX

PHONE

01622 842555

NEAR HERE

The Barrow House (p66)

Frankies Farmshop (p148)

The Dirty Habit (p55)

The Sportsman

PUBLIC HOUSES | WHITSTABLE | CT5 4BP

The Sportsman in Seasalter is an unlikely spot for a gastronomic delight but their reputation for fresh, quality fish is superb. The kitchen is run by Stephen Harris who has earned a Michelin star whilst cooking here. Stephen sources many quality ingredients from the local Monks Hill Farm.

The atmosphere is relaxed with well worn decor throughout, the energy here is focused entirely on the food they serve. The tasting menu is legendary, allow 3+ hours to work through the 10 courses. If you are a foodie then The Sportsman should be high up on your bucket list.

ADDRESS

Faversham Road
CT5 4BP

PHONE

01227 273370

NEAR HERE

The Old Neptune (p39)
Windy Corner Stores (p107)
Warehams (p136)

The Kings Head

PUBLIC HOUSES | WYE | TN25 5BN

The Kings Head is located in the historic village of Wye, at the foot of the Downs. They pride themselves on the quality of their food, service and environment. The pub interior is contemporary with soft cream and grey tones offset against chocolate leather banquette seating and stylish lighting.

In keeping with the countryside location, each of their guest rooms are simply and tastefully decorated. Wood panelling, reclaimed and vintage furniture is mixed with bright accents and modern accessories, to give the en-suite rooms a fresh and uncluttered feel. Breakfast is served in the restaurant.

ADDRESS

Church Street
TN25 5BN

PHONE

01233 812418

NEAR HERE

The Wife of Bath (p88)

Perry Court farm (p145)

The Wing (p165)

The Wheelwrights Arms

PUBLIC HOUSES | MATFIELD | TN12 7JX

The Wheelwrights Arms is a rustic and traditional pub exuding atmosphere and charm in the little village of Matfield. Candles and wood burners light up the farmhouse style interior and make it warm and welcoming. The menu has a focus on local and seasonal ingredients.

With excellent producers within a few miles around the village they source apples from local orchards, eggs, meat and asparagus from nearby farms. A front garden, embellished with overspilling hanging baskets of flowers is a pretty dining spot on a sunny day.

ADDRESS

The Green

TN12 7JX

PHONE

01892 722129

NEAR HERE

Star and Eagle (p59)

The Twenty Six (p77)

The Bicycle Bakery (p155)

The Goudhurst Inn

PUBLIC HOUSES | CRANBROOK | TN17 1DX

The Goudhurst Inn in Cranbrook is owned by the winery, Hush Heath Estate, in nearby Staplehurst. The pub's focus is centered on delicious wines and ciders from their winery and from around the world, as well as an array of craft beers, ales and spirits. All of their food is locally sourced.

The Bar provides snacks and sharing platters whilst The Hush Heath Room serves both an a la carte menu and a "Table D'hote" set menu that pairs each course with one of Hush Heath's wines or ciders. The Pizza and BBQ Shack in the garden serves freshly made clay oven pizzas and delicious BBQ dishes.

ADDRESS

Cranbrook Road
TN17 1DX

PHONE

01580 211451

NEAR HERE

The Milk House (p53)

The Three Chimneys (p43)

The Elephants Head (p71)

The Poet

PUBLIC HOUSES | MATFIELD | TN12 7JH

The Poet in Matfield has recently benefitted from a complete renovation. The restaurant sits within a 17th Century building named after war poet Siegfried Sassoon, who was born and raised in Matfield.

The kitchen is run by South African chef, Petrus Madutlela who focuses on the three pillars of quality, locality and seasonality. Dishes include 28 day aged rib eye with shallots, tuna tataki & blood orange sorbet. Non delinquent dogs are welcome.

ADDRESS
Maidstone Road
TN12 7JH

PHONE
01892 722416

NEAR HERE
Hush Heath Vineyard (p23)
The Velo House café (105)
Juliets (p109)

Ye Olde Yew Tree Inn

PUBLIC HOUSES | CANTERBURY | CT2 0HH

Ye Olde Yew Tree Inn is a 14th Century Inn located in the quintessential village of Westbere near Canterbury. The Inn was built in 1348 which makes it the oldest pub in Kent and legend has it that the pub was a regular haunt of highwayman Dick Turpin.

Ancient oak beams criss cross the dining room and an imposing inglenook fireplace adds to the atmosphere. There are two ghosts in residence who tend to make infrequent appearances. Prices are reasonable and dishes include Puff Pastry topped Beef and Mushroom Pie, Brie and caramelised Onion Tartlets and Mature Cheddar Ploughman's.

ADDRESS

32 Westbere Lane
CT2 0HH

PHONE

01227 710 501

NEAR HERE

Duke of William (p40)

Mama Feelgoods (p161)

Refectory Kitchen (p94)

The Freed Man

PUBLIC HOUSES | DEAL | CT14 7NX

The Freed Man is a micro-pub in the village of Walmer near Deal that opened in 2016 on the site of a former post office. The decor follows a nautical theme and the aim is to create a relaxed, social space for the local community that isn't restricted by being tied to a brewery.

If you are looking for a relaxed pint of local ale served by folk who know their beer then the Freed Man is for you. People and dog friendly, beards are optional.

ADDRESS

329 Dover Road
CT14 7NX

PHONE

07793 321126

NEAR HERE

Walmer Castle (p172)

The Court Yard Oyster Bar (p98)

Popup Cafe (p120)

The Milk House

PUBLIC HOUSES | SISSINGHURST | TN17 2JG

Situated in Sissinghurst, The Milk House is a village pub at the heart of the community. A former 16th century hall house, with timber beams and a Tudor fireplace, the pub serves a selection of local beers, cask ales and great wines by the glass, including several from the area's renowned vineyards.

Our spacious, light filled guest rooms have been styled with a touch of luxury and scenic views of the village and surrounding orchards. The Milk House sources their ingredients from a 20-mile radius, with local suppliers bringing them the freshest seasonal and ethical produce on a daily basis.

ADDRESS

The Street
TN17 2JG

PHONE

01580 720200

NEAR HERE

The Three Chimneys (p43)

Bloomsburys (p113)

Union Mill (p30)

The Falstaff

PUBLIC HOUSES | RAMSGATE | CT11 9JJ

The Falstaff in Ramsgate opened in 2015 after an extensive, 3 year renovation. This attractive and historic building was originally built in 1801 and is now home to a restaurant, store and boutique hotel.

Dining includes Steak burgers, Ham Hock Terrine and Wild Mushroom Risotto. There are eight rooms, each decorated with lovingly chosen vintage furniture and a private dining room. The Royal Harbour and the beach are but a short walk away.

ADDRESS
16-18 Addington Street
CT11 9JJ

PHONE
01843 482 600

NEAR HERE
Archive café (p88)

Wyatt and Jones (p92)

George and the Dragon (p65)

The Dirty Habit

PUBLIC HOUSES | HOLLINGBOURNE | ME17 1UW

The Dirty Habit is a beautiful old pub situated in the picturesque Kentish village of Hollingbourne and set within a designated area of outstanding natural beauty. Food is served all day and include Baked Camembert and Grilled halloumi & butternut squash salad.

The building has been completely restored while retaining the charming period features. Oak beams and inglenook fireplaces make this a delightful place to spend an afternoon. For the more active individual, bike rides and walks along the North Downs can be enjoyed from their doorstep.

ADDRESS

Upper Street
ME17 1UW

PHONE

01622 880 880

NEAR HERE

Leeds Castle (p164)

The Potting Shed (p58)

The Tickled Trout (p42)

The Potting Shed

PUBLIC HOUSES | LANGLEY | ME17 3LZ

The Potting Shed is the latest addition from the team at Elite Pubs. This is the fifth of their ventures and a great addition to the family. The pub is unique in the choice of interior being decorated with gardening tools, urns and other agricultural based paraphernalia.

Open from 8am breakfast with food served all day. Dishes include Superfood salad, Wood fired sourdough pizza and 35 day aged 10oz ribeye. Dishes change according to season and produce is always fresh and locally sourced.

ADDRESS

Sutton Road
ME17 3LZ

PHONE

01622 862 112

NEAR HERE

The Mulberry Tree (p99)

Frankies Farmshop (p148)

The Barrow House (p66)

Star and Eagle

PUBLIC HOUSES | GOUDHURST | TN17 1AL

The Star and Eagle is located in the pretty village of Goudhurst. Standing at 400ft above sea level, the hotel and pub restaurant has great views over the surrounding orchards, hop gardens and valley. Dating back to the 14th Century, it is believed to have once been an ancient monastery.

Relics of vaulted stonework are still visible in some parts of the building, alluding to its monastic history. The hotel and restaurant is traditional in style with dark timber beams, inglenook fires and low ceilings. The menu offers classic pub food with a continental twist.

ADDRESS

High Street, Cranbrook
TN17 1AL

PHONE

01580 211512

NEAR HERE

Hartley Coffee House (p154)

The Vineyard (p63)

Hush Heath Vineyard (p23)

Pearson's Arms

PUBLIC HOUSES | WHITSTABLE | CT5 1BT

Pearson's Arms in Whitstable is a traditional pub downstairs with a restaurant upstairs serving modern, wholesome, British cuisine, with a local and seasonal focus, created by chef Richard Phillips.

There is an open fire downstairs and the window tables upstairs offer exceptional views over the sea. Sun bleached wood clad walls and sky blue pendant lighting subtly reflect the natural environment of Whitstable. The ambience is relaxed and comfortable.

ADDRESS

Horsebridge Road
CT5 1BT

PHONE

01227 773133

NEAR HERE

The Sportsman (p46)

Hubbards Bakery (p158)

Whitstable Oyster Co (p86)

The Farm House

PUBLIC HOUSES | WEST MALLING | ME19 6NA

The Farm House, another member of the successful Elite Pub family, a village pub set within an Elizabethan House and situated in the heart of the old market town of West Malling, a historic market town North East of Royal Tunbridge Wells.

The bar area and beer garden are buzzy and the popular restaurant gets booked up for their breakfasts and Sunday Roasts. Favourites include Kentish game pie, slow cooked English lamb shoulder and king prawn linguine. But don't forget the sourdough Pizza served out back from their new Pizza Shack and Juice Bar.

ADDRESS
97 - 99 High Street
ME19 6NA

PHONE
01732 843 257

NEAR HERE
The Tickled Trout (p42)
Haywards Farmshop (p162)
Knole Park (p134)

The Star

PUBLIC HOUSES | **MATFIELD** | TN12 7JR

Nestled in the heart of the 'Garden of England', The Star is one of the three great pubs located in Matfield, a pretty little village near Tunbridge Wells. The pub has changed hands a few times in the past but now seems to have found its feet.

The menu makes the most of its surrounding countryside and proximity to locally produced ingredients. There are 3 log burning fires during the colder Winter months and during the Summer, you can enjoy their popular beer garden. On the first Saturday of every month they host live music.

ADDRESS

Maidstone Road
TN12 7JR

PHONE

01892 725458

NEAR HERE

The Poet (p50)

The Goudhurst Inn (p49)

Frankies Farmshop (p148)

The Vineyard

PUBLIC HOUSES | LAMBERHURST | TN3 8EU

Nestled by the historic Lamberhurst vineyards in the rolling Kent countryside, The Vineyard pub and restaurant is a rustic 17th century inn, exuding the influences of its surrounding environment. The Vineyard has an eclectic mix of natural materials, solid wooden furniture and vibrant leather armchairs.

The Vineyard serves traditional English cuisine and regional French brasserie style fare with local and regional ingredients featuring strongly. Wine is very much central to The Vineyard and the featured wine list is a true reflection of a specially curated assortment from around the world.

ADDRESS

The Down
TN3 8EU

PHONE

01892 890222

NEAR HERE

The Elephants Head (p71)
The Queen's Inn (p74)
The Milk House (p53)

The Wheatsheaf

PUBLIC HOUSES | HEVER | TN8 7NU

The Wheatsheaf is believed to have been built at the end of the 14th century. Clues to its age have been found within the pub, including a rare medieval crown post in the timbers. In Tudor times, it was a splendid hunting lodge serving Hever Castle, rumoured to have been a favourite retreat of Henry VIII.

The timbered dining room with a huge roaring fire is an idyllic place to enjoy the fine selection of food, which focuses on locally sourced, quality ingredients. On sunnier days sit on the outside terrace with a glass of their sparkling wine, sourced from Bluebell Vineyard just 18 miles away.

ADDRESS
Hever Road
TN8 7NU

PHONE
01732 700100

NEAR HERE
Hever Castle (p173)
Eat 'n' Mess (p121)
The Beacon (p78)

George and the Dragon

PUBLIC HOUSES | SANDWICH | CT13 9EJ

The George and Dragon pub in Sandwich has built a name for itself as one of the best places to eat in town. The roaring fire, attentive service and top quality cuisine make this a must when visiting the town. Built in 1446, this historic pub features light wooden beamed ceilings and a stone interior wall.

Tucked around the back of the town near the Parish Church, this delightful pub is best booked in advance to avoid disappointment. With their dinner menu, they have matched beers to each dish and also have a carefully considered wine list.

ADDRESS

24 Fisher St, Sandwich
CT13 9EJ

PHONE

01304 613106

NEAR HERE

The Falstaff (p54)

The Corner House (p96)

No Name Shop (p151)

The Barrow House

PUBLIC HOUSES | **EGERTON** | **TN27 9DJ**

A much loved village pub with a stylish overhaul. The Barrow House was crafted in 1576 using timbers from sailing ships. The pub serves its local community well, providing good seasonal food and a relaxing place to unwind. Their handcrafted burgers are made in house and their bread is baked daily.

Idyllic in its countryside location, enjoy real ale and filling yet refined fare. Decor is immaculate, merging modern style with country accents. For those who want to spend more time in the village or explore the local area, there are three beautiful bedrooms upstairs.

ADDRESS
The Street
TN27 9DJ

PHONE
01233 756599

NEAR HERE
The Dirty Habit (p55)
Frankies Farmshop (p148)
Hush Heath Vineyard (p23)

he White Hart

BLIC HOUSES | SEVENOAKS | TN13 1SG

s old coaching inn has been nourishing travellers for over three dred years and you'll find character and charm at every turn. m a roaring fireplace to a sunny garden, discover a great spot to oy their menu which focuses on quality ingredients and a fusion British and global dishes.

e pub's name is inspired by the legend of The White Hart (a hart is ale deer). The Gin list is pretty impressive, with over 20 to choose m. Fresh flowers and candles decorate the simple wooden tables. gs of a good nature are allowed in the bar and garden areas.

ADDRESS

Tonbridge Road
TN13 1SG

PHONE

01732 452022

NEAR HERE

The Wheatsheaf (p64)

Hever Castle (p73)

The Farm House (p61)

Leicester Arms

PUBLIC HOUSES | TONBRIDGE | TN11 8BT

The Leicester Arms is an historic pub in the medieval village of Penshurst. Oak beams, leather sofas and a crackling fireplace all add to the authenticity of the ambience and charm. Dating back to the 16th century, this dog friendly coaching inn remains the social hub of the village and a popular destination from London weekenders.

Dishes include roast sirloin of Sussex beef, steak & Spring onion jam sandwich and Harvey's beer battered Fish & chips. This pub makes an ideal stop off when visiting nearby Penshurst Place.

ADDRESS

High Street, Penshurst
TN11 8BT

PHONE

01892 871617

NEAR HERE

The Twenty Six (p77)

Tonbridge Castle (p28)

The Tulip Tree (p127)

Abbot's Fireside

UBLIC HOUSES | ELHAM | CT4 6TD

uilt as an Inn in 1452, Abbot's Fireside, with its black and white
udor exterior is rich in history. Push open the wooden door and
ou will find yourself surrounded by antique furniture and original
aded glass windows.

he lounge and restaurant feature huge fireplaces and upstairs are
even guest rooms available on a B&B basis. Lunches and dinners
e available as well as popular Sunday Roasts.

ADDRESS

High St, Elham, Canterbury
CT4 6TD

PHONE

01303 840566

NEAR HERE

Folkestone Harbour (p21)

Rocksalt (p76)

The Wife of Bath (p88)

Sankey's

PUB | TUNBRIDGE WELLS | TN4 8AA

Situated in the heart of Tunbridge Wells Sankey's Public House is a family run pub set within the ground floor of a Victorian manor house. Dishes include fresh oysters and lobster as well as firm favourites of fish & chips Sankey's Smokie and home smoked fish cakes.

Sustainability of their ingredients is paramount as are the quality and variety of beer on offer with 23 on draught with their selection of craft beer being updated regularly. Also within the Sankey's family is Sankey's Brasserie which specialises in fresh fish and shellfish from around the British coast.

ADDRESS	PHONE
39 Mount Ephraim	01892 511422
TN4 8AA	

The Hooden on the Hill

PUB | ASHFORD | TN24 0NY

Hooden on the Hill is a traditional family run country pub boasting characterful features such as flagstone floors, wooden beams and wood burning stove.

They pride themselves on holding the "Cask Marque" accreditation and feature a guest ale once a week. Food is locally sourced and is transformed into good quality traditional pub grub. The huge beer garden is a perfect sun trap for all the family.

ADDRESS	PHONE
24 Silver Hill Road	01233 662226
TN24 0NY	

The Elephants Head

PUB | TUNBRIDGE WELLS | TN3 8LJ

The Elephants Head is an historic timbered Wealden Farmhouse on the Kent/Sussex border, east of Tunbridge Wells and a genuine English pub.

The pub has been taken over by a new landlord, Dave Stanley who keeps the beer in check and the fire well stocked within this listed building. Owned by Harvey's Brewery, this is more of a drinking den and so not particularly child friendly. There is also a large garden for those sunny afternoons.

ADDRESS

Furnace Lane
TN3 8LJ

PHONE

01892 739525

The Peacock Inn

PUB | CRANBROOK | TN17 2PB

Located in Goudhurst, a quiet country village in Kent, The Peacock Inn is a family run, 14th century country pub, with an emphasis on locally sourced fresh food, beer and wine. With an open fire and summer garden, the pub creates a relaxing environment whatever the season.

Nestled in Kent's scenic countryside, The Peacock boasts a wine cellar of carefully curated brands. Shepherd's Neame brewery's collection of beers featuring classical, heritage and modern varieties are also on the menu.

ADDRESS

Goudhurst Road
TN17 2PB

PHONE

01580 211233

The Queen's Inn

PUBLIC HOUSES | CRANBROOK | TN18 4EY

This immaculately restored inn provides a luxurious country retreat to eat, drink and indulge. The Queen's Inn can be found in the scenic town of Cranbrook. Fresh, locally sourced ingredients are expertly combined and served in their stylish, yet welcoming surroundings.

They offer an extensive handpicked wine list, a range of local beer, ale and cider, all served next to their roaring log fire. Guest rooms are available and have been elegantly designed and finished, with each individually styled to create its own personality and story.

ADDRESS

Rye Road
TN18 4EY

PHONE

01580 754233

The Black Horse

PUBLIC HOUSES | PLUCKLEY | TN27 0QS

The Black Horse at Pluckley is a spacious and authentic English pub. Built in the 1470's, the pub was originally a dry moated farmhouse for the wealthy Dering Family. This beautiful beamed country pub boasts five log burning fires and is ideally sited for the breathtaking walks around Pluckley.

Responsibly farmed and locally sourced produce is used to make freshly cooked meals. The pub played the location for The Hare and Hounds in the television series The Darling Buds of May. Pluckley is reputedly the most haunted village in England and this is claimed to be the most haunted pub in Kent.

ADDRESS

The Street
TN27 0QS

PHONE

01233 841948

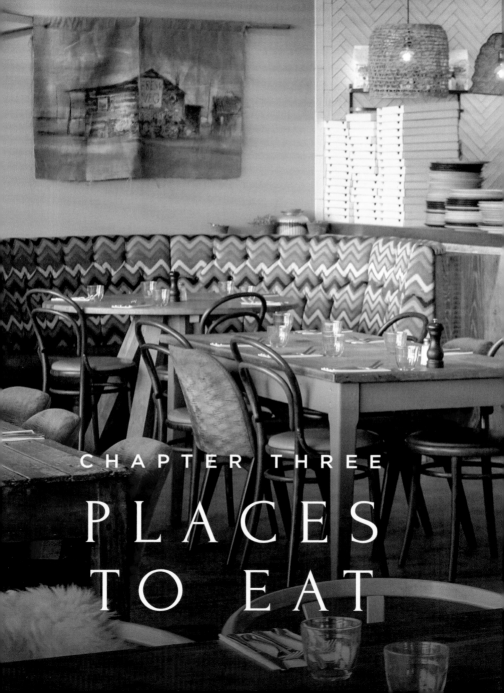

CHAPTER THREE

PLACES TO EAT

Rocksalt

PLACES TO EAT | FOLKESTONE | CT19 6AA

On a sunny afternoon, finer views are hard to find in Folkestone than those to be had from Rocksalt. This modern restaurant overlooks the busy little harbour and specialises in the day's catch by local fisherman wherever possible.

Run by Mark Sargeant, one-time head chef at Claridge's, the sleek glass structure is cantilevered off the harbour wall and provides a sophisticated addition to this seaside town. Dishes include Lobster & Salmon Pasty, Cucumber Cured Mackerel and Potted Dungeness Shrimps.

ADDRESS
4-5 Fish Market
CT19 6AA

PHONE
01303 212070

NEAR HERE
The Pullman (p44)
The Café Collective (p114)
Thackerays (p85)

The Twenty Six

PLACES TO EAT | SOUTHBOROUGH | TN4 0RX

The Twenty Six is an enchanting restaurant on the outskirts of Tunbridge Wells in Southborough. The twenty-six seats give the restaurant its name and the high ceilings and tasteful furnishings are reminiscent of a restaurant in the mountains of Austria. This is the test kitchen of Chef Scott Goss.

With stripped wood floor and tables, exposed brick walls and hanging pendant light bulbs, the creative menu changes daily. Goss likes to keep the ingredients seasonal whilst his wine menu features artisanal, natural and biodynamic options. Wood burners and candles keep the restaurant cozy and ambient.

ADDRESS

15A Church Road
TN4 0RX

PHONE

01892 544607

NEAR HERE

The Beacon (p78)

The Velo House café (105)

Juliets (p109)

The Beacon

PLACES TO EAT | TUNBRIDGE WELLS | TN3 9JH

The Beacon is a stylish, contemporary restaurant with mesmerising views over the valley and onwards to Tunbridge Wells. Open, roaring fires, rustic furnishings and flickering candles make the space cozy and welcoming. They have kept their menu simple, with great attention to the quality of the ingredients.

On a fine day, the elevated decking with panoramic views makes for an excellent space to dine Al Fresco or have a relaxed drink in the sun. The menu changes seasonally and is always inspired by the environment. Set in seventeen beautiful acres with three lakes, The Beacon is an inspiring place to visit.

ADDRESS

Tea GaRoaden Lane
TN3 9JH

PHONE

01892 524252

NEAR HERE

The Wheelwrights Arms (p23)

Juliets (p109)

The Wheatsheaf (p35)

Googies

Googies began serving high quality hand roasted coffee. It quickly became a popular spot to sample their award winning burgers and smoked meats. The interior is rustic and stripped back with wood floors and filament light bulbs.

Their burgers celebrate the best of Kentish produce including Dexter beef from Sladden Farm in the Alkham Valley, Canterbury cobble cheese and smoked bacon from CA Worgans butchers in Canterbury. They also stock a wide range of craft beers, many of which are kept on tap.

ADDRESS

15 Rendezvous St
CT20 1EY

PHONE

01303 246188

NEAR HERE

Rocksalt (p76)

Cullin's Yard (p66)

The Wing (p165)

The Secret Garden

PLACES TO EAT | MERSHAM | TN25 6NH

As the name suggests, the Secret Garden, has just that - a beautiful walled garden to admire whilst enjoying brunch, afternoon tea, or an evening meal. The unique Pudding night - held once a month, has been created for those with a sweet tooth with an array of puddings and custards to try on the night, and also including a pudding based quiz.

Open for breakfast, lunch and dinner and late for cocktails.

ADDRESS

Hythe Road
TN25 6NH

PHONE

01233 501586

NEAR HERE

The Wife of Bath (p88)

Thackerays (p85)

Woolpack Inn (p41)

Le Pinardier

PLACES TO EAT | DEAL | CT14 6EE

Le Pinardier, French for "Wine Shop" feels like stepping into a beautiful French wine cellar. It is a shop, wine bar, music venue and art gallery in Deal. This is an intimate venue that tries and often succeeds to be many things. Wine is sold by the bottle and the glass.

Cheese plates, charcuterie and paté with baguettes are available to accompany the wine, which is sold by knowledgeable staff. This is the concept of the passionate founders of Frog and Scot, a contemporary French bistro situated close to Le Pinardier.

ADDRESS

102 High Street
CT14 6EE

PHONE

01304 372788

NEAR HERE

Popup Cafe (p120)

George and the Dragon (p65)

Deal Castle (p171)

GB Pizza Co

PLACES TO EAT | MARGATE | CT9 1DH

After touring the country with their pizza van, Rachel and Lisa set up shop on the shorefront of Margate, with almost immediate success. Thanks to their passion for quality and foodie backgrounds (award winning chef and restaurant critic), they have received endless praise for their outstanding pizzas.

Sunday Times listed it in the top 25 UK Pizzerias. It has also featured in the Observer, Telegraph, Time Out and Red Magazine. They use British, seasonal produce as much as they can. Their sauce is homemade and slow-cooked and their dough is made to their exact recipe (it took three months to perfect).

ADDRESS

14 Marine Drive
CT9 1DH

PHONE

01843 297700

NEAR HERE

The Greedy Cow (p98)

Kingsgate and Botany Bay (p142)

The Corner House (p96)

Wheelers Oyster Bar

PLACES TO EAT | WHITSTABLE | CT5 1BH

Wheelers Oyster Bar is the oldest and perhaps the smallest restaurant in Whitstable. People come from far and wide to sample their small, seasonal, seafood menu with ingredients sourced locally. The dining room seats twelve at most which only adds to its unique ambience.

The sourcing of their ingredients is of paramount importance, even to the point where they have developed their own local organic garden, producing salad, herbs and fresh fruit. Local fisherman work very hard to get them the best produce they can. No alcohol is served, so bring your own.

ADDRESS

8 High Street
CT5 1BH

PHONE

01227 273311

NEAR HERE

The Old Neptune (p39)

Windy Corner Stores (p107)

David Brown Delicatessen
(p149)

Luben's Pizza

PLACES TO EAT | FOLKESTONE | CT20 1EZ

An effortlessly stylish tiled exterior is home to Luben's Pizza. This modern restaurant is a popular place to enjoy authentic, artisanal pizzas from their wood fired oven. The restaurant is decorated with industrial furnishings and features a deli table stacked high with breads and antipasti.

Inside Luben's restaurant is a contemporary and airy interior complete with natural accents and a green color palette. Rustic wooden tables are embellished with garlic and chilli oils and the open kitchen allows you to see your pizza being prepared.

ADDRESS

24 Rendezvous Street
CT20 1EZ

PHONE

01303 487110

NEAR HERE

The Smokehouse (p67)

The Pullman (p44)

Rocksalt (p76)

Saltwood on the Green

PLACES TO EAT | HYTHE | CT21 4PS

Saltwood on the Green focuses on simplicity and pristine ingredients, believing that if they do the hard work up-front by carefully choosing their suppliers and ingredients and work with the seasons, the dishes will create themselves.

Housed in the village's former General Store, built in 1900, the building has undergone a long restoration process which now showcases original pine flooring, sash windows and the store's original shelving across an entire wall. Their wine features selected favourites from English and Kent vineyards.

ADDRESS

The Green
CT21 4PS

PHONE

01303 237800

NEAR HERE

Rocksalt (p76)

Cullin's Yard (p66)

The Wing (p165)

Whitstable Oyster Co

PLACES TO EAT | WHITSTABLE | CT5 1BU

Hailed as one of the country's finest seafood restaurants, Whitstable Oyster Fishery Co is based within a former oyster store on the seafront. Tracing its origins back to the 1400s, it is one of the oldest companies in Europe, with a long, rich history of farming the famous Royal Whitstable Native Oyster.

In the 1850s, the company was sending as many as 80 million oysters a year to Billingsgate market in London. Fresh oysters are their speciality with other seafood dishes including classics such as Cod and Chips and Chargrilled Razor Clams. The food is kept simple with an emphasis on quality ingredients.

ADDRESS

Horsebridge Road
CT5 1BU

PHONE

01227 276856

NEAR HERE

The Sportsman (p46)

The Carriage Restaurant (p95)

The Goods Shed (p143)

The West House

The West House in Biddenden is a small, family run and Michelin starred restaurant located within a 16th century weaver's cottage. Run by head chef, Graham Garrett, the focus is on exceptional, seasonal ingredients that are locally sourced wherever possible.

The restaurant gained a Michelin star after its first year in 2004, and has held it ever since. Featured in Harden's top restaurants list and holding 3 AA Rosettes, Graham has been awarded Best Chef in Kent. He has cooked at both 10 Downing Street and at a private dinner for Her Majesty, the Queen.

ADDRESS

28 High Street
TN27 8AH

PHONE

01580 291341

NEAR HERE

Bloomsburys (p113)

The Goudhurst Inn (p49) (p24)

The Milk House (p53)

The Wife of Bath

PLACES TO EAT | WYE | TN25 5AF

The Wife of Bath is a highly regarded, contemporary restaurant serving Northern Spanish inspired dishes and is home to five beautiful en-suite bedrooms. A fusion of rustic and refined, the menu is innovative and utilises the best seasonal produce available, both locally and direct from Spain.

The A La Carte menu takes inspiration from Cataluña, The Basque Country, Cantabria and Galicia. The classic building has been tastefully decorated with soft tonal colours, simple wooden tables, exposed brick walls and a decorative tiled floor by the bar. The guest rooms are also beautifully appointed.

ADDRESS

4 Upper Bridge Street
TN25 5AF

PHONE

01233 812232

NEAR HERE

The Kings Head (p47)

The Secret Garden (p80)

Perry Court farm (p145)

Royal Harbour Brasserie

PLACES TO EAT | RAMSGATE | CT11 9RN

With an unrivalled position on the harbour arm in Ramsgate, the Royal Harbour Brasserie does a fine job at recreating the style of an original Parisienne brasserie. The brasserie's unique position offers panoramic views of busy Ramsgate marina, the jetty and out to sea.

French classics such as moules mariniere and home-baked patisseries are available to eat either inside or, if weather permits, outside on the large terrace. Take a leisurely stroll along the harbour arm or drive down the pier to the brasserie. Friendly dogs are welcome. On a sunny day, there are few spots with better sea side views.

ADDRESS
Harbour Wall
CT11 9RN

PHONE
01843 599 059

NEAR HERE
The Falstaff (p54)

The Corner House (p96)

GB Pizza Co (p82)

Wyatt and Jones

PLACES TO EAT | BROADSTAIRS | CT10 1EU

At Wyatt and Jones, menus change with the seasons and their produce is sourced locally. They have an extensive list of Kentish drinks and wines and only use local fishermen and butchers. Lobster, when in season, is caught half a mile away and delivered straight from the boat to their door.

Locality of ingredients is a priority with Kentish beer and local fish featuring prominently including Monkfish and Roasted Red Pepper Ceviche and Anchovy Toast. Great for their sea views and child friendly too, this is a welcoming and popular Kent gem.

ADDRESS

23 - 27 Harbour Street
CT10 1EU

PHONE

01843 865 126

NEAR HERE

GB Pizza Co (p82)
Royal Harbour Brasserie (p89)
The Corner House (p96)

The Allotment

PLACES TO EAT | DOVER | CT16 1DP

The Allotment in Dover, is an innovative restaurant that prides itself on serving quality British cuisine, with ingredients sourced straight from the allotment of the owner and locally. With a vibrant cream, wood clad interior and a multitude of pendant lights, the ambience is contemporary and sophisticated.

The large, partly stained glass window allows lots of natural light to flood into the restaurant whilst chalk boards detail the specials. The menu includes a range of meat, fish and vegetarian options with a seasonal approach. The Sunday roast is popular, as are the opulent desserts.

ADDRESS

9 High St
CT16 1DP

PHONE

01304 214467

The George Vaults

PLACES TO EAT | ROCHESTER | ME1 1LN

The George Vaults boasts a vaulted Crypt dating back to 1325. Originally known as Saint George and Dragon, the building burned down in 1768 and the present structure was created over the vault. Today the venue is a contemporary brasserie and wine bar with distinctive architecture and preserved history.

This unique venue can be privately hired for events and is even licensed for wedding ceremonies within their 14th century vault. The brasserie's a la carte menu serves dishes created from locally sourced ingredients. Traditional Sunday roasts are also served.

ADDRESS

35 High St
ME1 1LN

PHONE

01634 817165

Refectory Kitchen

PLACES TO EAT | CANTERBURY | CT2 8AF

The Refectory Kitchen in Canterbury is a contemporary, family run bistro. Their diverse menu is kept simple and local where possible. Sandwiches include Roast Pork Belly and Chorizo or twists on the classics such as Smoked Fish Fingers.

Juice is squeezed on site, coffee is made properly and the wood burner will keep you cosy. If the sun is shining then you can eat al fresco and watch the world go by. Iconic movie posters are scattered over brick walls and the ambience is relaxed.

ADDRESS

16 St. Dunstans St,
Canterbury
CT2 8AF

PHONE

01227 638766

Samphire

PLACES TO EAT | WHITSTABLE | CT5 1BQ

Samphire is a Kentish Bistro firmly established within the Whitstable restaurant scene. Their style of food is simple with emphasis on great produce. They proudly showcase the best seasonal, traceable ingredients sourced from local farms, allotments and producers. Their menus change regularly.

Friendly and welcoming, Samphire is another great addition to the long list of quality eateries to choose from in Whitstable. The contemporary interior features farmhouse, mismatched style furniture, fused with sleek artwork and furnishings. Menus are detailed on chalkboards.

ADDRESS

4 High St, Whitstable
CT5 1BQ

PHONE

01227 770075

The Carriage Restaurant

PLACES TO EAT | FAVERSHAM | ME13 8PE

The Carriage Restaurant is a small friendly restaurant, located within The Railway Hotel, Faversham. After the success of their coffee shop Jittermugs, just a short walk down the road. Nick and Julia opened The Carriage Restaurant in 2015. The restaurant features railway memorabillia.

The interior is simple with muted red and green walls, stripped wooden flooring and vintage luggage featured on shelving. The menu is small, features local ingredients wherever possible and changes regularly.

ADDRESS

The Railway Hotel, Preston Street, Faversham
ME13 8PE

PHONE

N/A

Willows Secret Kitchen

PLACES TO EAT | CANTERBURY | CT1 2PH

Willows Secret Kitchen in Canterbury is all about cheese and great coffee. A hot sandwich iron weighing 1.5kg creates their "Amazing Grilled Cheese Sandwiches". They use coffee supplied by Hasbean & New Town, along with various micro roasters from around the country.

The café is simple inside with dark grey/blue and white walls, a small industrial style kitchen and vintage food and coffee accessories. Old treacle jars hold sugar and metal and wood crates act as shelves. You can eat in or take away.

ADDRESS

42 Stour St, Canterbury
CT1 2PH

PHONE

01227 788777

The Corner House

PLACES TO EAT | MINSTER | CT12 4BZ

The Corner House, Minster, is a critically acclaimed restaurant serving quality, homemade British food in a relaxed ambience. The menu is big on sharing with delights such as Romney Marsh Lamb and Venison scotch egg. Bread is made fresh on site each morning.

Deeson's

PLACES TO EAT | CANTERBURY | CT1 2HX

Deeson's is a bistro style restaurant providing traditional British fine dining in the heart of Canterbury and in the shadow of the spire of the cathedral. The environment is relaxed and they source their ingredients locally with a large part of their menu grown or reared on their small holding.

Pork & Co.

PLACES TO EAT | CANTERBURY | CT1 2HX

Pork & Co serve free range, fourteen hour slow roast pork on homemade, brioche buns with crackling and coleslaw. The welfare of the animals is a priority and they make an effort to educate people about the origins of their meat. This is a welcome stop off for aficionados of meat.

Zeus

PLACES TO EAT | CANTERBURY | CT1 2JA

The Zeus Ouzeri & Taverna is a family owned restaurant making fresh, authentic Greek cuisine in the heart of Canterbury. This contemporary restaurant is minimal in style with light woods and white walls featuring Greek Warriors.

The Pound

PLACES TO EAT | **CANTERBURY** | CT1 2BZ

The Pound at One Pound Lane in Canterbury is home to The Pound Bar & Kitchen, situated within a listed former police station. The original features of the gaol are maintained and played on wherever possible, with the option of dining within a former police cell.

The Ambrette

PLACES TO EAT | **CANTERBURY** | CT1 2NY

Chef Dev Biswal has won multiple awards for his adventurous and artistic flair, fusing a mix of local and exotic ingredients to create unique dishes at his Ambrette Restaurants. The Ambrette Canterbury is set within the historic city walls on Beer Cart Lane. It is walking distance from Canterbury Cathedral.

The Forge

PLACES TO EAT | **WHITSTABLE** | CT5 1BX

The Forge in Whitstable is a licensed seaside shack selling fish and chips and oysters straight off the fishing boats. Displaying the catch in open ice crates with blackboards detailing the prices, there are picnic tables outside to sit and enjoy your selection.

Wee Willy Winkles

PLACES TO EAT | **WHITSTABLE** | CT5 1AB

Wee Willie Winkles is a crab and winkle restaurant next to the fishing harbour of Whitstable. Situated in the old railway turntable there is a takeaway fish and chip shop downstairs alongside the fish market and a restaurant upstairs.

The Greedy Cow

PLACES TO EAT | MARGATE | CT9 1ER

The Greedy Cow is one of Margate's favourite eateries with renowned classics such as their famous Greedy Cow Burgers and luxurious Caramel Brownies. Their menu includes vegetarian options such as Falafel and Halloumi, alongside their 100% beef burgers.

The Court Yard Oyster Bar

PLACES TO EAT | DEAL | CT14 7BW

The Court Yard, Oyster Bar & Restaurant in Deal has a great menu that changes with the daily local catches. 60% of the menu is seafood, so if you want to experience some fantastic local fish, this is a wise choice.

Olivers

PLACES TO EAT | ROCHESTER | ME1 1EY

Enjoy dishes such 8oz Centre Cut Fillet Steak, Oven poached fillet of salmon and Slow Roasted five spice duck legs. Dont forget the impressive drinks menu with over 30 Cocktails and 45 wines.

Cullin's Yard

PLACES TO EAT | DOVER | CT17 9BY

Step inside Cullin's Yard restaurant, and you'll think you've boarded a ship of yesteryear. Located within a converted ship yard, the restaurant specialises in fresh fish which is handy given it is located by the Marina.

Hythe Restaurant

PLACES TO EAT | DOVER | CT21 6AW

The Hythe Bay Seafood Restaurant at Dover is in an unrivalled position, with the beach directly under the panoramic windows, which stretch the whole length of the restaurant. All food is from sustainable sources and Griggs of Hythe bring their daily deliveries of fish caught along the south east coast.

Olive e Capperi Trattoria

PLACES TO EAT | ROCHESTER | ME1 1PY

Olive e Capperi pizzeria is a traditional, authentic Italian pizzeria located in the heart of Rochester. Dishes include homemade lasagna and paccheri pasta with aubergine cream. Camillo & Costa work hard to recreate the Italian family kitchen in this corner of Kent.

The Smokehouse

PLACES TO EAT | FOLKESTONE | CT19 6NN

The Smokehouse in Folkestone is the newest member of Mark Sargeant's restaurant family serving "proper" fish & chips with a modern ethos. Recently voted as one of the 30 best chippies in Britain by The Times, the smokehouse relies on the daily catch in order to decide what will be on the menu.

The Mulberry Tree

PLACES TO EAT | MAIDSTONE | ME17 4DA

This stylish country restaurant offers a wonderfully relaxing experience complete with modern interiors and refined cuisine. The cuisine is 'modern British and European,' using seasonal, free-range and organic produce that is sourced from local suppliers in Kent.

CHAPTER FOUR

CAFÉS

Jittermugs

CAFÉS & TEA ROOMS | FAVERSHAM | ME13 8NZ

Jittermugs is a small, popular coffee shop with a variety of homemade cakes, including gluten-free and vegan options. In the evenings they open as a candlelit wine bar and offer tasty tapas, continental beers and flowing beats.

Jittermugs has a large brick fireplace with a cozy woodburner to warm the toes. Wooden floors, ceramic brick tiles and Penguin book details, make this a relaxed and warm environment. Seating is available outside for warmer days.

ADDRESS

ME13 8NZ

PHONE

01795 533121

NEAR HERE

Shepherd Neame Brewery (p31)

The Carriage restaurant (p95)

Macknade Fine Foods (p144)

Old Fire Station

CAFÉS & TEA ROOMS | TONBRIDGE | TN9 1BH

The Old Fire Station has been a cornerstone building in Tonbridge's history since it first opened its doors in 1901. In service until 1983, its grand facade and stoic presence has remained an architectural gem of the town. Today the building hosts exciting pop-ups and tailor made one off events.

In 2015, Richard Collins began turning his dream of making the building a modern and vibrant community space into a reality. From the beginning, the space has championed many independant restaurants, boutiques and businesses and given them a platform to showcase their talent.

ADDRESS

Castle Street
TN9 1BH

PHONE

N/A

NEAR HERE

Tonbridge Castle (p28)

Juliets (p109)

The Velo House café (105)

The Velo House Café

CAFÉS & TEA ROOMS | TUNBRIDGE WELLS | TN4 9TN

The Velo House in Tunbridge Wells is a cycling mecca with a café and shop dedicated to the love of bikes and cycling. The Velo House has been created by cyclists for cyclists. The large open café downstairs is a creative and original way of combining a great little eatery and specialist bike shop.

Dishes include the house special 'Velo' Burger, Spicy Quesadillas and Mac 'n Cheese. You can relax and enjoy your coffee as your bike is in the workshop getting attention from their professional mechanics. The shop upstairs offers a range of carefully curated, high-end road bikes, clothing and accessories.

ADDRESS
5 St John's Road
TN4 9TN

PHONE
01892 554500

NEAR HERE
Basil (p108)
The Beacon (p78)
Arte Bianca (p157)

Waterlane Coffeehouse

CAFÉS & TEA ROOMS | CANTERBURY | CT1 2NQ

Water Lane Coffeehouse is an independant coffee house in the heart of Canterbury. Serving a range of the best coffees available, they also work with local producers to offer a regularly changing menu of baked goods and homemade cakes. All of their coffee is ethically sourced with full traceability.

The interior is relaxed and welcoming with old Chesterfield sofas, industrial lighting and oak flooring. The café overlooks the river Stour, so makes a lovely setting for your morning caffeine fix. They say that they try to be as environmentally friendly as possible in their approach to business.

ADDRESS
Water Lane
CT1 2NQ

PHONE
01227 464797

NEAR HERE
Refectory Kitchen (p94)
Micro Roastery (p126)
Café St. Pierre (p129)

Windy Corner Stores

CAFÉS & TEA ROOMS | WHITSTABLE | CT5 1DZ

Windy Corner Stores in Whitstable is an understated café/restaurant that prides itself on selling the best of Kent's produce. The Guardian voted it one of the top ten budget restaurants on the North Kent coast.

The interior is simple and relaxed. Quality coffee and their homemade cakes are a popular choice and the menu offers interesting options such as chicken & chard fajitas and goats cheese and butterbean tortilla.

ADDRESS

110 Nelson Road
CT5 1DZ

PHONE

01227 771707

NEAR HERE

David Brown Delicatessen
(p149)

Wheelers Oyster Bar (p83)

Frank (p141)

Basil

CAFÉS & TEA ROOMS | TUNBRIDGE WELLS | TN1 1LJ

With a philosophy of creating deliciously wholesome food, indulgent cakes and really great coffee, Basil has become a hugely popular independant café group in Tunbridge Wells. Their raw ingredients are conscientiously sourced, with all of their eggs and meat being free range and organic when possible.

Believing strongly in supporting local farmers, growers, bakers and butchers, they have been voted as one of the ten best coffee shops in Kent by the Index Magazine and have received great praise for all three of their cafés by locals.

ADDRESS
1-3 Lime Hill Road
TN1 1LJ

PHONE
01892 541566

NEAR HERE
The Twenty Six (p77)
The Velo House café (105)
The Bicycle Bakery (p155)

Juliets

CAFÉS & TEA ROOMS | TUNBRIDGE WELLS | TN1 1XF

Juliets in Tunbridge Wells is a haven for lovers of hearty, healthy food followed by a serious slice of cake. Its brick wall interior, low pendant lighting and open counter full of superfood salads are offset against a window bursting with vibrant homebaked cakes.

The lunch menu changes daily, with stews, salads and sandwiches available. A tempting breakfast menu starts from 8am. Vintage china lines the shelves and serves their array of teas and coffees. Healthy, fresh smoothies are also available.

ADDRESS

54 High Street
TN1 1XF

PHONE

01892 522931

NEAR HERE

Arte Bianca (p157)

Shrager's Patisserie (p153)

Leicester Arms (p68)

Waterloo House Tea Room

CAFÉS & TEA ROOMS | CRANBROOK | TN17 3JA

Waterloo House Tea Room is situated in the peaceful, medieval town of Cranbrook and is renowned for its traditional teas and homemade cakes. Dishes are created with locally sourced ingredients where possible. The relaxed ambience and friendly service make it a popular local spot.

The exposed brick walls and wood cladding in muted shades are offset by rustic dark wood beams. Outside there are several tables for al fresco lunching on warmer days.

ADDRESS
1 Waterloo Road
TN17 3JA

PHONE
01580 713802

NEAR HERE
The Milk House (p53)
Bloomsburys (p113)
Biddenden Vineyard (p24)

Fuggles Beer Café

CAFÉS & TEA ROOMS | TUNBRIDGE WELLS | TN1 2AP

Fuggles Beer Café was established in 2013 with the aim of specialising in the best of British and European beers. Good Beer Guide listed and runner-up in the Observer Food Monthly Awards 2015/2016, the bar also offers gins and whiskies accompanied by some of the best British cheeses and cured meats.

Known for working with local & national microbreweries, orchards, vintners and distillers in order to provide a mighty fine drink when you visit, the extensive selection of quality drinks is also an important part of the Fuggles philosophy. Casual and relaxed in atmosphere.

ADDRESS

28 Grosvenor Road
TN1 2AP

PHONE

01892 457739

NEAR HERE

The Velo House café (105)

The Beacon (p78)

The Elephants Head (p71)

Ted's Room

CAFÉS & TEA ROOMS | CRANBROOK | TN17 3HF

Ted's Room is a casual, cosy and warm café located in Cranbrook. World travel paraphernalia decorates the room with postcards, world maps and vintage car models embellishing the walls.

Ted's Room is also a popular meeting spot for locals, with Ted himself often found working the coffee machine or mixing a milkshake. The comfy soft leather chairs, fresh flowers and globe string lights create a relaxed atmosphere.

ADDRESS
11-13 Stone Street
TN17 3HF

PHONE
01580 720880

NEAR HERE
Union Mill (p130)
The Milk House (p53)
Waterloo House Tea Room
(p110)

Bloomsburys

CAFÉS & TEA ROOMS | BIDDENDEN | TN27 8DQ

Bloomsburys has established itself as one of the most exclusive Glampsites to stay in the UK. Using a combination of beautiful Yurts, Soul pad tepees, a majestic Sioux tepee and a large Safari lodge, they are able to cater for a wide variety of occasions from romantic breaks to weddings.

Bloomsburys café and restaurant reflects a fusion of colourful, eclectic styles. Their ethos is to create the highest quality, freshly prepared food and drink in a relaxing environment. They take pride in serving the very finest freshly ground coffee which is also offered for sale in the shop.

ADDRESS
Sissinghurst Road
TN27 8DQ

PHONE
01580 292992

NEAR HERE
The Three Chimneys (p43)
The Tiny Teapot (p131)
Hush Heath Vineyard (p23)

The Café Collective

CAFÉS & TEA ROOMS | FOLKESTONE | CT20 1RL

The Café Collective is a social enterprise located on the attractive Old High Street in Folkestone which serves freshly ground coffee, tortilla pizzas and crêpes. The café aims to provide a community for local coffee lovers, artists, musicians, and more.

These guys are coffee lovers who take great care in selecting a new roast each month from an independant, Canterbury based roaster. If you are serious about your coffee then this relaxed little coffee shop is for you.

ADDRESS

43 The Old High Street
CT20 1RL

PHONE

N/A

NEAR HERE

Beano's Vegetarian café (p130)

The Pullman (p44)

Rocksalt (p76)

Nutmeg Café

CAFÉS & TEA ROOMS | TENTERDEN | TN30 6BW

you are looking for a slice of cake and a cup of artisan coffee, then
utmeg in Tenterden is a welcome stop off. Their menu is made up
f fair trade and environmentally friendly dishes. As well as cakes
nd sandwiches they sell homemade filo tarts, hearty stews and
roper sausage rolls.

opular with the locals, Nutmeg has a rustic charm and is
onveniently located in the heart of town. The deli counter is packed
ith tasty dishes and they have a wide selection of cheeses and
udges organic breads too. Cheese and meat boards are available.

ADDRESS

3 Sayers Lane
TN30 6BW

PHONE

01580 764125

NEAR HERE

Chapel Down Vineyard (p25)

Bluebell Coffee House (p126)

Bloomsburys (p113)

The Veg Box Café

CAFÉS & TEA ROOMS | CANTERBURY | CT1 2HG

The Veg Box Café is a relaxed, independant café in the heart of Canterbury that specialises in veggie, vegan, fairtrade and organic dishes. Situated near the cathedral gate, this busy little café is the creation of the passionate owners, Liz and Adam.

Breakfasts and lunches are created daily on the premises. Dishes include raw lime and coconut cheesecake and cashew butter Pad Thai. This is a lovely space to unwind and re-energise with some tasty, wholesome treats.

ADDRESS

17A Burgate
CT1 2HG

PHONE

01227 456654

NEAR HERE

Micro Roastery (p126)

Waterlane Coffeehouse (p106)

The Goods Shed (p143)

Archive Café

AFÉS & TEA ROOMS | **RAMSGATE** | **CT11 9LG**

Archive Homestore & Kitchen is a design-led lifestyle store offering a unique and fresh collection of interesting and beautiful homewares and food and drink. Archive Kitchen champions local growers and producers by offering a range of healthy lunches and cakes as well as specialty coffee and local juices.

Set under an old brick archway on the Kent coastline, this timber-lined shop and café takes its design cues from Scandinavian architecture and traditional beach huts. They use the space to showcase some of their favourite British and Scandinavian brands.

ADDRESS

17 Military Road
CT11 9LG

PHONE

01843 580666

NEAR HERE

Vinyl Head café (p118)

The Falstaff (p54)

The Corner House (p96)

Vinyl Head Café

CAFÉS & TEA ROOMS | RAMSGATE | CT11 9JN

Vinyl Head Café is a record shop and café with a curated portfolio of vinyls availble to buy, whilst others vibrantly embellish the walls. With decks on the counter playing popular tunes, they serve delicious coffee, cakes and other light bites in a friendly and buzzy environment.

There's an eclectic mix of furniture and memorabilia, as well as occasional live performances. Fresh juices and vegan options are available and served by charming staff. The café attracts a diverse and friendly crowd in this relaxed environment.

ADDRESS

Addington Street
CT11 9JN

PHONE

N/A

NEAR HERE

No Name Shop (p151)

The Salutation Gardens (p32)

The Harbour café (p122)

The Cake Shed

CAFÉS & TEA ROOMS | TUNBRIDGE WELLS | TN2 5TN

The Cake Shed Café is home to some of the best coffee and homemade cake in Tunbridge Wells. Offering a selection of small-batch, freshly baked cakes from their open kitchen, light lunch options of house salads, soups and sandwiches are also available. A lovely setting, with great attention to detail.

Exhibiting the work of local artists and frequently hosting live music events, The Cake Shed is located within the pretty Pantiles area. The interior is rustic with vintage wooden crates for shelving, wooden farm tables and a buzzy counter, brimming with the daily offerings.

ADDRESS

32 The Pantiles, Tunbridge Wells
TN2 5TN

PHONE

01892 457357

NEAR HERE

Basil (p108)

Thackerays (p85)

Fuggles Beer Cafe (p111)

Popup Café

CAFÉS & TEA ROOMS | DEAL | CT14 7AE

Popup Café in Deal is a quality driven café serving speciality coffee, freshly baked sourdough bread, delicious brunches, lunches and a selection of bakes. All made in house. They bake their bread and use a long fermentation, natural yeasts and organic flour to create the perfect batch.

Popup Café occasionally stays open later into the evening, serving a supper menu. These meals use ingredients that are freshly picked, freshly cooked and locally sourced. Every meal uses several local suppliers according to what is freshest and best. Selected wines are also available by the glass.

ADDRESS

16 High St, Deal
CT14 7AE

PHONE

N/A

NEAR HERE

Deal Castle (p171)

Le Pinardier (p81)

The Black Douglas (p129)

Eat 'n' Mess

CAFÉS & TEA ROOMS | SEVENOAKS | TN13 1AU

Eat'N'Mess in Sevenoaks, creates opulent cakes, artisan breads and specialist coffee within their bustling and intimate café. With gluten and dairy free options available, the counter is piled high with appetizing cakes and brownies, all displayed beautifully on cake stands and wooden crates.

Bespoke, occasion cakes are a speciality of Eat'N'Mess and with two weeks notice they can create decadent cakes for events, from weddings and christenings to birthday parties. Whether you like buttercream or fondant, Eat'N'Mess will artfully and passionately create something deliciously unique.

ADDRESS
67 London Rd, Sevenoaks
TN13 1AU

PHONE
01732 461 839

NEAR HERE
The White Hart (p67)

The Farm House (p61)

Haywards Farmshop (p162)

The Harbour Café

CAFÉS & TEA ROOMS | MARGATE | CT9 1EZ

The Harbour Café in Margate is directly on the seafront with tremendous views over the water. High ceilings, brick walls, stripped back floors, large light filled windows and tables embellished with fresh flowers, make this café the perfect place to watch life on the seafront with a coffee.

The Harbour Café is located close to the Turner Gallery, making it a popular choice with those visiting the contemporary space. The feature of the interior is their interesting long counter, clad with mosaic tiles, to a backdrop of their wines and coffee beans.

ADDRESS
10 The Parade
CT9 1EZ

PHONE
01843 290110

NEAR HERE
Turner Contemporary (p169)
GB Pizza Co (p82)
The Greedy Cow (p98)

Cocolicious

CAFÉS & TEA ROOMS | **CRANBROOK** | TN17 3HF

Cocolicious is a pâtisserie and coffee shop owned by the passionate Lucinda Hamilton, in the heart of Cranbrook. Their homemade cakes are delicious, their coffee is sourced from a West Sussex based roastery and their bread is brought in daily from a local small batch micro bakery, using organic ingredients.

The interior is painted in creamy whites and highlighted with vintage pinks, fresh flowers and pretty cake stands. At Cocolicious they say the essence of the pâtisserie café is simple. It's about delicious food made with skill & care, using the tastiest ingredients and served with love.

ADDRESS

Stone Street
TN17 3HF

PHONE

01580 714954

Scallywag Café

CAFÉS & TEA ROOMS | **TUNBRIDGE WELLS** | TN4 8AA

By day, Scallywag Café in Tunbridge Wells is a peaceful and relaxing space to escape for coffee and homemade brownies. By night it becomes a cabaret destination where artists, creatives, musicians and visionaries play. Wines are complemented by a selection of small plates and desserts.

The venue is eclectic in style and has a shabby chic lounge style of interior with a mini grand piano, lampshaded lights, wooden floors with rugs and plenty of comfortable seating. Large windows allow the light to flood in by day and in the evening the ambience comes alive when it has its musical nights.

ADDRESS

45 Mount Ephraim Road
TN4 8AA

PHONE

01892 315281

Bluebell Coffee House

CAFÉS & TEA ROOMS | TENTERDEN | TN30 6BW

The Bluebell coffee house is a new additio to the Tenterden scene and is a homely ca serving proper coffee, hot chocolate, panir and cakes. Great coffee, great service ar pleasant surroundings are what they prie themselves upon.

With a counter full of cupcakes, decade chocolate cakes and other sweet indulgence you can also enjoy their cream teas or fre bean coffee. Eclectic furniture decorates th interior and its relaxed atmosphere makes family friendly. Gluten free options are availab

ADDRESS

7 Sayers Square
TN30 6BW

PHONE

01580 761112

Micro Roastery

CAFÉS & TEA ROOMS | CANTERBURY | CT1 2T

The Micro Roastery in Canterbury is independant coffee shop creating some the best coffee in town. Coffee sacks ar contemporary art highlight the interior of th understated café. Bar stools and comfy, cushie clad benches provide casual places to sit whil you drink your chosen coffee.

They roast their own beans in small batche to maintain the freshness and source on seasonal basis. When we visited, the bea selection included Guatemalan, Rwandan ar Mexican varieties. They use 90 espresso bear for a single shot of espresso as opposed to th industry standard of 42.

ADDRESS

4 St Margaret's Street
CT1 2TP

PHONE

01227 634419

Baps & Bloomers

CAFÉS & TEA ROOMS | SANDWICH | CT13 9BY

Baps and Bloomers in Sandwich has hit the town by storm since opening in October 2015. Artisan baker Paul Usherwood produces the daily batches; his degree in food science and baking technology, plus 30 years experience, makes his some of the best bread around.

As well as bread, they serve a fine choice of pastries and sweet bites too. The store is designed with a minimalist approach. White walls and wood crates display the freshly baked produce and silver cake stands display the sweeter temptations. The produce is the focus.

ADDRESS

6 King Street
CT13 9BY

PHONE

07711 132960

The Tulip Tree

CAFÉS & TEA ROOMS | CHIDDINGSTONE | TN8 7AH

The Tulip Tree tea room and gift shop in Chiddingstone is reputedly the oldest working shop in the UK, dating back to 1453. Situated in the converted coach house, the interior features a beautiful counter, surrounded by white washed bricks and industrial pendant lights which hang from beneath the beams.

The tea rooms also feature a beautifully refurbished garden, serving up homemade breakfasts, lunches and afternoon teas outside on warm days. From scones, meringues and brownies to wonderful creative cake creations, they additionally host a monthly themed pop-up restaurant in the evening.

ADDRESS

3 The Village
TN8 7AH

PHONE

01892 871504

Whitstable Coffee Co.

CAFÉS & TEA ROOMS | WHITSTABLE | CT5 1AP

Whitstable Coffee Company is an independant coffee shop in the heart of Whitstable serving delicious coffees, teas, sandwiches and picnic fillers. There is a contemporary style inside with a soft challky green counter and glass deli fridge, displaying their freshly prepared baguettes and salads.

Whistable Coffee Company also serve their homemade cakes and a selection of smoothies. Take away one of their creamy coffees and walk along the seafront, or in the Summer, stock up on picnic foods for a beach picnic.

ADDRESS
39 High Street
CT5 1AP

PHONE
01227 280844

The Bakehouse at 124

CAFÉS & TEA ROOMS | TONBRIDGE | TN9 1AS

The Bakehouse at 124 is part of a fast-growing artisan food revival that brings an exceptional taste and experience to eating that modern production methods fail to match. Fresh bread and baked goods are created every day in small batches. Ingredients are sourced as locally as possible.

The unique Toast Bar allows you to take a few slices of heaven with you, or enjoy them whilst watching the artisan bakers at work in the bakery kitchen. Relax in a cosy sofa next to the woodburner or sit up at the bar to get a closer look. A feast for the eyes as well as your tastebuds.

ADDRESS
124 High Street
TN9 1AS

PHONE
01732 360382

Café St. Pierre

CAFÉS & TEA ROOMS | CANTERBURY | CT1 2BG

Café St. Pierre in Canterbury is a traditional French café/bistro in the heart of Kent. They recently celebrated their 20th year of business, reinforcing their continued popularity and success. The interior is eclectic and characterful with vintage model cars decorating the window.

Café Mauresque

CAFÉS & TEA ROOMS | CANTERBURY | CT1 2JR

Café Mauresque is an atmospheric Andalucían/North African oasis located in the heart of the historic City of Canterbury. Escape the hustle and bustle of Canterbury's cobbled streets and be swept below into their intimate, lantern lit cellar restaurant. The restaurant has a warm friendly atmosphere.

Hope & Lane Café

CAFÉS & TEA ROOMS | DEAL | CT14 6EG

Hope & Lane Café in Deal is a trendy café with vintage industrial styling, using only the freshest locally sourced ingredients and only the best coffee beans (Peruvian Tunki). They serve up a wide choice of pastries and sandwiches, as well as quality breakfasts, which have received great praise.

The Black Douglas

CAFÉS & TEA ROOMS | DEAL | CT14 6JB

The Black Douglas Coffee House is founded on the principles of good simple food, sourcing locally or direct from the producer with an emphasis on traceable and sustainable produce. On Friday and Saturday evenings they offer a small menu with two options for each course, depending on what is in season.

Boho

CAFÉS & TEA ROOMS | CANTERBURY | CT1 2AZ

Boho Café in Canterbury is a family run, bohemia styled, friendly and intimate Café on Canterbury Hig Street. Their menu changes regularly with a focus o fresh local ingredients served in their own unique style Their menu selects the best dishes from Britain an France.

Beano's Vegetarian Café

CAFÉS & TEA ROOMS | FOLKESTONE | CT20 1JT

Beano's Vegetarian Café is an eclectic little busines located in the heart of the Creative Quarter. Surrounde by artists and designers, this area of Folkestone i becoming a hive of creativity and, in turn, this café ha a strong local fan base.

Mary's Tea room

CAFÉS & TEA ROOMS | DYMCHURCH | TN29 0LD

On the edge of Dymchurch and a short stroll from th sea is Mary's traditional tea room. Popular with bot the local community and visitors alike, it's a traditiona tea room in every sense; from the embroidered table cloths, bone china tea sets and loose leaf tea itself.

Stag Coffee

CAFÉS & TEA ROOMS | ASHFORD | TN24 8SD

Stag Coffee is a new independant coffee shop o Ashford High Street. This family run business i passionate about crafting outstanding coffee an delicious food. Freshly prepared quiches and spicy halloumi paninis together with chocolate brownies an victoria sponge are just some of the delicacies on offe

The Deaf Cat

CAFÉS & TEA ROOMS | ROCHESTER | ME1 1LX

The Deaf Cat Gallery & Studios aims to provide a creative space to Rochester based artists and to serve a proper cup of coffee. Blood red chesterfield sofas make this a comfortable coffee stop in which to slow down and take in some local art. Wheelchair and buggy friendly.

The Seaplane Works

CAFÉS & TEA ROOMS | ROCHESTER | ME1 1JT

A recent addition to the coffee shop scene in Rochester is The Seaplane Works. This rustic little café serves modern vegan and vegetarian food within a modern, pared down interior. Great for those with food intolerances and the all important wifi is free.

Bruno's Bakes and Coffee

CAFÉS & TEA ROOMS | ROCHESTER | ME1 1PT

Bruno Breillet, master patissier, chocolatier and founder of Bruno's Bakes and Coffee, grew up in Lyon, a city at the epicentre of French gastronomy. Drawing his experience and techniques from watching his mother and grandmother in the kitchen, his café has won a total of five "Great Taste Award" stars.

The Tiny Teapot

CAFÉS & TEA ROOMS | BIDDENDEN | TN27 8AL

The Tiny Teapot is a traditional tea room, located in the English countryside village of Biddenden in Kent. This family run tea room serves loose-leaf tea and homemade soups, sandwiches and cakes, all made on site by the owner Christine and her daughter, using locally sourced ingredients where possible.

CHAPTER FIVE
SHOPS

Margate Retro

SHOPPING | MARGATE | CT9 1DA

Margate Retro is a haven for everything retro, from furniture and clothing to a wide selection of vibrant neon signage. Margate Retro is spread over 3 sites around Margate old town which includes their main store 'Margate Retro' and their holiday apartments 'Margate Retro Rooms'.

The apartments are fully furnished and decorated with eccentric retro furnishings, as well as some quirky extras including an original vinyl jukebox in the bedroom, a fruit machine and Space Invaders table.

ADDRESS

King Street
CT9 1DA

PHONE

N/A

NEAR HERE

Turner Contemporary (p169)

Margate Beach (p33)

GB Pizza Co (p82)

Warehams

SHOPPING | WHITSTABLE | CT5 1DA

Warehams in Whitstable is one of many antique treasure chests offering antique garden ornaments and gustavian furniture. They believe that the simplicity of the design and the unique patina of the aged, painted wood gives a design its uniqueness. They source and sell statement pieces.

The Gustavian furniture, which they specialise in, is the style of decor used in Swedish palaces as early as 1780 and is also more commonly known today as 'shabby chic'.

ADDRESS

68 Oxford Street
CT5 1DA

PHONE

N/A

NEAR HERE

Chappell Contemporary (p180)

Frank (p141)

The Old Neptune (p39)

The Yarn Dispensary

SHOPPING | FAVERSHAM | ME13 7AG

This 'luxury yarn dispensary' is a new arrival in Faversham, but despite its innovative approach it has the comforting feel of a welcoming shop that has been perfecting its trade for decades, or even centuries. Seasoned knitters will find colourful fabrics and paraphernalia aplenty.

Frequent workshops cater for all abilities, while exhibitions of clothing collections ensure there's something warm, soft and beautiful even for stubborn non-knitters. With wonderful quality ranges and the chance to try out their wares, this is a truly artisanal experience.

ADDRESS

6 Market Place
ME13 7AG

PHONE

01795 597700

NEAR HERE

Macknade Fine Foods (p144)

The Sportsman (p46)

The Goods Shed (p143)

Adrian Harrington Rare Books

SHOPPING | TUNBRIDGE WELLS | TN1 1YQ

Adrian Harrington has been selling rare books since 1971. Dealing in a wide selection of literature from modern first editions, leather bound library sets, childrens' and illustrated books to fine and rare antiquarian books, they also offer a full and expert bookbinding and restoration service.

Ian Fleming bibliographer Jon Gilbert curates their world-class stock of James Bond material, including first edition novels, film posters, original scripts and associated ephemera. This is a treasure trove for collectors and literary enthusiasts.

ADDRESS
20-22 Chapel Place
TN1 1YQ

PHONE
01892 547531

NEAR HERE
Juliets (p109)
Basil (p108)
The Twenty Six (p77)

Hot Salvation Records

SHOPPING | **FOLKESTONE** | **CT20 1EZ**

Hot Salvation Records curate the very best in new and used vinyl from their Folkestone shop. They also operate their own independant record label, focusing on fast paced Punk with their bands including Cosmic Thoughts, Mass Lines and Sans Pareil.

This is a fine addition to the Folkestone shopping scene and one which stocks a wide selection of musical genres. They also serve freshly ground coffee and herbal tea so grab a cup, choose a few tunes and take your time.

ADDRESS

32 Rendezvous Street
CT20 1EZ

PHONE

01303 487657

NEAR HERE

Folkestone Harbour (p21)

Beano's Vegetarian café (p130)

The Café Collective (p114)

Stevenson Brothers

SHOPPING | ASHFORD | TN26 3AP

A highly esteemed company with a rich history of tradition and craftsmanship. Stevenson Brothers is a bespoke rocking horse company that hand-carves each piece in the countryside of Kent. Founded by twin brothers over 30 years ago, this company has built an impressive following of loyal customers.

The company have made pieces for Queen Elizabeth II crafted from English oak from Windsor Great Park. Visiting the workshop in Kent is a special experience and allows you to see the exquisite craftsmanship in detail. You can even design your own rocking horse.

ADDRESS

Ashford Road
TN26 3AP

PHONE

01233 820363

NEAR HERE

Silcocks Farm Shop (p152)

Shepherd Neame Brewery (p31)

The Barrow House (p66)

Frank

SHOPPING | **WHITSTABLE** | CT5 1AG

Frank was founded with an aim to sell the work of British printmakers, designers and craftspeople. Celebrating the homegrown creativity of the newly fledged, as well as more firmly established practitioners. Handmade prints, drawings and papercuts exist alongside ceramics, jewellery, stationery and books.

A white and airy interior is offset against vibrant artwork, colourful cards and imaginative gifts. Beautifully curated and merchandised, the store is the perfect place to visit for a unique gift or the discovery of an up-and-coming artist.

ADDRESS

65 Harbour Street
CT5 1AG

PHONE

01227 262500

NEAR HERE

Shepherd Neame Brewery (p31)

Samphire (p94)

Windy Corner Stores (p107)

CHAPTER SIX
FOOD SHOPS

The Goods Shed

FOOD SHOPS | **CANTERBURY** | CT2 8AN

The Goods Shed is a daily farmers' market, providing the best from Kent's 'Garden of England'. The on-site restaurant with its open kitchen, serves distinctive dishes created from ingredients sourced from the market. Candlelit in the evening or suffused by sunlight, the restaurant is full of ambience.

The characterful station building highlights its Victorian features from rustic brick walls to dramatic arched windows. Naturally seasonal produce ranges from pressed juices and organic vegetables to fish and charcuteries. The finest local suppliers showcase their ingredients here.

ADDRESS

Station Road
CT2 8AN

PHONE

01227 459153

NEAR HERE

Café St. Pierre (p129)

Waterlane Coffeehouse (p106)

The Veg Box Café (p116)

Macknade Fine Foods

FOOD SHOPS | FAVERSHAM | ME13 8XF

Macknade Fine Foods is one of the largest food halls in the South East having been set up as a family business in 1979. It continues to be run by the same family who aim to provide the "best food and drink shopping experience" possible.

Judging by their popularity and their Retailer of the Year award at the Taste of Kent Awards 2017, they are certainly doing something right. There is a deli, butcher and coffee shop on site and they have recently been granted an extended licence so keep an eye out for supper clubs and wine tasting evenings.

ADDRESS
Selling Road
ME13 8XF

PHONE
01795 534497

NEAR HERE
The Carriage Restaurant (p95)
Jittermugs (p103)
The Yarn Dispensary (p137)

Perry Court Farm

FOOD SHOPS | **ASHFORD** | **TN25 4ES**

Perry Court Farm has been growing wonderful fruit and vegetables in a responsible and environmentally friendly way for three generations. The farm now produces over 200 varieties of English crops, the majority of which they supply direct to the consumer through their farmer's markets and their farm shop.

The farm shop and café is located in the Stour Valley, surrounded by traditional apple and pear orchards, fields of fresh vegetables and summer fruits, all of which are available in the farm shop. There is freshly baked bread every morning and a Cheese Room boasting over 100 varieties of English cheeses.

ADDRESS

Canterbury Road
TN25 4ES

PHONE

01233 812302

NEAR HERE

The Wife of Bath (p88)

Stevenson Brothers (p140)

The Secret Garden (p80)

Frankies Farmshop

FOOD SHOPS | STAPLEHURST | TN12 0JT

Frankie's Farmshop and café is part of Staplehurst Nurseries. You are invited to browse and select the finest local produce and seek inspiration from their team for your next dinner party. Artisan bread is baked from scratch and you can soak up the delicious smells emanating from their open kitchen.

Each product sold in the shop and café has been handpicked for its flavour, quality and provenance. Honey-glazed baked ham, pâté and a selection of award-winning British and Continental cheese are available to enjoy alongside cured meats, antipasti, fresh fruit and vegetables and a multitude of condiments.

ADDRESS

Clapper Lane
TN12 0JT

PHONE

01580 890713

NEAR HERE

Hush Heath Vineyard (p23)

Leeds Castle (p164)

The Tickled Trout (p42)

David Brown Delicatessen

FOOD SHOPS | WHITSTABLE | CT5 1AH

The David Brown Delicatessen is renowned for fine service and quality supplies. With pastries and bread made by the man himself, this independant delicatessen has become a fine food magnet for the people of Whitstable and its visitors.

Situated in an old butchers shop, the deli has built a strong reputation. Its simple yet stylish interior houses shelves of condiments, a curated collection of wines and breads and pastries piled high on top of their marble counter. Bowls of vibrant salads displayed in the windows lure people in.

ADDRESS

28A Harbour Street
CT5 1AH

PHONE

01227 274507

NEAR HERE

Samphire (p94)
Whitstable Oyster Co (p86)
Wee Willy Winkles (p97)

Peter Speaight Butchers

FOOD SHOPS | TUNBRIDGE WELLS | TN1 1YQ

Peter Speaight Butchers is a popular independant store in Tunbridge Wells, renowned for its quality local meat, vegetables and homemade sausages. Peter Speaight's passionate approach and thirty years of experience have given him national recognition.

The store also supplies fresh fruit, locally produced condiments, honey, and freshly baked artisanal bread. Beautifully designed with a large sweeping glass deli counter, stripped wooden floors and a feature chandelier, the store is a favourite local spot.

ADDRESS

15 Chapel Place
TN1 1YQ

PHONE

01892 616668

NEAR HERE

The Beacon (p78)

The Bicycle Bakery (p155)

Scallywag café (p123)

No Name Shop

FOOD SHOPS | SANDWICH | CT13 9AJ

The No Name Shop in Sandwich is a fantastic delicatessen offering a great choice of fine French cheeses, olive oils, charcuterie, freshly baked breads and patisseries. Coffees and cakes are also available. The delicatessen has the ambience of a French market store with wooden crates displaying the produce.

Just above the shop is their restaurant, Le Bistro, serving typically French fare using the fresh produce sold in the shop. Dishes include Croque Monsieur and amazing cheese boards. The restaurant and shop are situated in one of the oldest buildings in Sandwich on 'No Name Street', giving it its quirky name.

ADDRESS

1 No Name Street
CT13 9AJ

PHONE

01304 612626

NEAR HERE

Baps & Bloomers (p127)

George and the Dragon (p65)

The Salutation Gardens (p32)

Silcocks Farm Shop

FOOD SHOPS | TENTERDEN | TN30 6TL

Silcocks Farm shop is situated in a light filled converted barn. They sell meat and dairy products from animals born and reared on the farm. They only use local abattoirs approved by the Soil Association. Meat is hung in their own cool room and butchered in their cutting room, adjacent to the shop.

When the sun is shining, enjoy sitting outside in their lovely courtyard and in the winter feel the warmth of their cosy wood burning stove as you relax inside on a comfy sofa. They serve delicious homemade and farm sourced food in their café.

ADDRESS

Grange Road
TN30 6TL

PHONE

01580 763351

NEAR HERE

Stevenson Brothers (p140)

Bluebell Coffee House (p126)

Chapel Down Vineyard (p25)

hrager's Patisserie

rager's Patisserie was established by television chef Rosemary rager and is housed in a beautiful regency building in the Lower antiles of Tunbridge Wells. Popular with the locals, people come om far and wide to sample the cakes created by Paris-trained astry chef Marc Mouzon.

shes include Paris Brest and light mousses, cheesecakes, croque bouche, macarons, tarts and cakes such as Gateaux Opera, arjolaine and Lemon Tart. Mouzon was previously head pastry ef at the Michelin star restaurant, Le Royal Champagne in France.

ADDRESS

26-28 The Pantiles
TN2 5TN

PHONE

01892 548358

NEAR HERE

Peter Speaight Butchers (p150)

The Twenty Six (p77)

The Elephants Head (p71)

Hartley Coffee House

FOOD SHOPS | CRANBROOK | TN17 3QG

Hartley Coffee House & Farm Shop is located on the outskirts of Cranbrook. It's split into separate sections and sells an abundance of locally sourced fresh fruit and vegetables, meat from local farms butchered in Tenterden, a wine cellar specializing in English wines, plants and flowers and a popular coffee shop.

The coffee shop overlooks their working apple orchards and includes a sun-terrace; a perfect spot for light lunch on a warm day. Hartley Coffee House is open Mon – Fri 8am till 6pm and 10 till 4 on Sundays.

ADDRESS
Hartley Road
TN17 3QG

PHONE
01580 715233

NEAR HERE
The Goudhurst Inn (p49)
The Milk House (p53)
The Three Chimneys (p43)

The Bicycle Bakery

FOOD SHOPS | TUNBRIDGE WELLS | TN1 2QZ

The Bicycle Bakery in Tunbridge Wells is an authentic bakery where fresh bread is made on site daily. If you are into your artisan sour dough, then this is the place for you. The bicycle inspired interior adds to the charm, with a full-size bike and a basket brimming with homebaked loaves in the window.

Cakes and pastries are all made on site alongside an array of carefully crafted teas and coffees. The café is small with limited seating but on warmer days the roadside, outside tables are perfect for people-watching over a latte.

ADDRESS

120 Camden Road
TN1 2QZ

PHONE

01892 514255

NEAR HERE

The Poet (p50)
The Velo House Cafe (p105)
The Vineyard (p63)

Perfect Partners

FOOD SHOPS | CRANBROOK | TN17 3HF

Perfect Partners is a hidden gem in the town of Cranbrook. Specialising in unusual wines and cheeses, this small but ambitious store sells a diverse range of local produce. Selling cheeses from over fifteen countries, you can usually taste before you buy.

The shop is only 190 square foot but with the 40 years of experience the proprietors have, they source their collection of produce with passion. Everything from patés and chutneys to sundried tomatoes and olive oils, quality here is the key.

ADDRESS

7 Stone Street
TN17 3HF

PHONE

01580 712633

NEAR HERE

Hartley Coffee House (p154)

Biddenden Vineyard (p24)

The Peacock Inn (p71)

Arte Bianca

FOOD SHOPS | TUNBRIDGE WELLS | TN1 1YQ

Arte Bianca is a family run, authentic Italian delicatessen, located Chapel Place, Tunbridge Wells. Great coffee, meats and large mozzarella ciabattas are their specialities and Gianni and Angela are often on hand to give you an Italian welcome.

The delicatessen counter is filled with olives, stuffed peppers, sun-dried tomatoes and other authentic Italian dishes. Olive oils and Italian condiments line the shelves. The large glass frontage is the perfect spot to sit with one of their popular coffees and watch the world go by.

ADDRESS

1 Chapel Place
TN1 1YQ

PHONE

01892 510554

NEAR HERE

Shrager's Patisserie (p153)

Basil (p108)

The Bicycle Bakery (p155)

Hubbards Bakery

FOOD SHOPS | WHITSTABLE | CT5 1AP

Hubbards of Whitstable is a traditional bakery selling an inspiring range of freshly baked breads, cakes, doughnuts and biscuits. The presentation is tempting and there are numerous organic options. Staff are friendly and knowledgeable.

Their iced treats are particularly popular with the little ones and their prices are very reasonable. Queues come out the door on Saturdays, so get there early for their freshly baked produce straight out of the oven.

ADDRESS

63 High Street
CT5 1AP

PHONE

01227 772060

NEAR HERE

David Brown Deli (p149)

Samphire (p94)

The Old Neptune (p39)

W.J. Crouch Butchers

FOOD SHOPS | **BEARSTED** | **ME14 4DN**

W.J. Crouch Butchers are proud distributors of locally sourced Beef, Lamb and Pork. You quickly notice in their Bearsted store that they sell far more than quality meats.

You'll find freshly baked breads and pastries, homemade quiches, a fine selection of speciality cheeses, together with a choice of wine and beers and other products from the area.

ADDRESS
1-2 The Parade, The Green
ME14 4DN

PHONE
01622 737130

NEAR HERE
The Dirty Habit (p55)
The Potting Shed (p58)
Leeds Castle (p164)

Austen's of Rochester

FOOD SHOPS | ROCHESTER | ME1 1EU

Austen's of Rochester is a family run business originally opened as a high quality greengrocers which has rapidly expanded, due to demand, to include an all local line-up of free range meat and chicken, award winning artisan breads and cheeses, eggs, juices, dairy, wholemeal foods and more.

Austen's has an immaculate in-store offering. Visiting farms every week, they sample the produce and ensure the standards and ethics are consistently high. They know where all the local foods they supply have come from and, with most of it, which fields it was grown in.

ADDRESS

137B High Street
ME1 1EU

PHONE

01634 838775

NEAR HERE

Olive e Capperi Trattoria (p9￼

Rochester Castle (p175)

Bruno's Bakes and Coffee (p13￼

Mama Feelgoods

FOOD SHOPS | BEKESBOURNE | CT4 5EU

Mama Feelgoods is a charming fine food store. Located in the quaint village of Bekesbourne, this shop is a wonderful place to find organic and locally sourced produce and homebaked cakes. Situated within an original stables and cattle yard, the interior has retained its oak beams and character.

Freshly baked bread, old fashioned sweets and specialty cheeses are available alongside other delicatessen foods and condiments. The café serves breakfasts and lunches created from fresh, seasonal, local produce. Coffee served with one of their indulgent cakes is another popular option.

ADDRESS
Bekesbourne Lane
CT4 5EU

PHONE
01227 830830

NEAR HERE
Duke of William (p40)
The Goods Shed (p143)
The Beaney House (p170)

Haywards Farmshop

FOOD SHOPS | TONBRIDGE | TN11 0AH

At Haywards Farmshop in Tonbridge Kent you will find an extensive range of fresh fruit, vegetables and meat all grown and produced to a very high standard. Their aim is to provide their customers with the best local Kent produce and specialty foods.

The store is contemporary in design and displays the colourful produce in large overspilling wooden crates painted in soft colours. Large glass counters are full of locally produced, free range meat which is served by knowledgeable staff.

ADDRESS

Tonbridge Road
TN11 0AH

PHONE

01732 850354

NEAR HERE

The Bakehouse at 124 (p128)

The Tickled Trout (p42)

Old Fire Station (p104)

CHAPTER EIGHT

CULTURE

Leeds Castle

CULTURE | MAIDSTONE | ME17 1PL

Leeds Castle has been a Norman stronghold, the private property of six of England's medieval queens, a palace used by Henry VIII and his first wife Catherine of Aragon, a Jacobean country house, a Georgian mansion and an elegant early 20th century retreat for the influential and famous.

In the 21st century, Leeds Castle has become one of the most visited historic buildings in Britain. Historic properties within the Leeds castle estate can be hired as guest accommodation, from Glamping in the castle vineyard and a Knight's Cottage to the 16th century Maiden Tower.

ADDRESS

Maidstone
ME17 1PL

PHONE

01622 765400

NEAR HERE

The Potting Shed (p58)

The Dirty Habit (p55)

The Barrow House (p66)

The Wing

CULTURE | FOLKESTONE | CT18 7EU

Built in 2015, The Wing is a project owned by the Battle of Britain Memorial Trust. The building was constructed to mimic the shape of a Spitfire wing and is a interactive space to learn about this combat of the Second World War.

From statues to replica aircraft, this is an educational attraction. Experience what it was like for a pilot in the 1940 battle, through the interactive video facility. A central 'cockpit' area with an open balcony offers superb views across the Channel to France, from where the Luftwaffe appeared.

ADDRESS
New Dover Road
CT18 7JJ

PHONE
01303 249 292

NEAR HERE
Folkestone Harbour (p21)
Lower Leas Coastal Park (p33)
The Pullman (p44)

Marlowe Theatre

CULTURE | CANTERBURY | CT1 2AS

The Marlowe Theatre is an award winning, 1,200 seat theatre in the heart of Canterbury. The theatre was completely rebuilt in 2011 and their programme now includes the National Theatre, the Royal Shakespeare Company and the Glyndebourne Touring Opera.

Productions range from West End musicals to international ballet. Whether you're looking for a light lunch, or the full pre-show dining experience, they offer good food, made from the best locally sourced ingredients in their Green Room restaurant which has views of the river Stour and Canterbury Cathedral.

ADDRESS

The Friars
CT1 2AS

PHONE

01227 787787

NEAR HERE

The Beaney House (p170)

The Goods Shed (p143)

Westgate Towers Museum (p177)

Turner Contemporary

CULTURE | MARGATE | CT9 1HG

Turner Contemporary is one of the UK's leading art galleries, offering diverse exhibitions of contemporary and historical art. The Turner Contemporary has free admission and is located directly on the seafront, on the site where Turner would stay when visiting the town.

The gallery opened in 2011, designed by Sir David Copperfield. The beauty of the building is enhanced by the natural light, which pours through the windows dramatically. The views out to sea are spectacular. The gallery has regular educational activities and events and an attractive café.

ADDRESS
Rendezvous
CT9 1HG

PHONE
01843 233000

NEAR HERE
Margate Beach (p33)
Kingsgate and Botany Bay (p11)
The Harbour café (p122)

The Beaney House

CULTURE | CANTERBURY | CT1 2RA

The Beaney House of Art and Knowledge is the central museum, library and art gallery of Canterbury. Housed in a Grade II listed building, this award winning facility provides state-of-the-art exhibition galleries, excellent educational facilities and a varied programme of events.

The building takes its name from its benefactor, Dr James George Beaney, who died in 1891 and left money in his will to the city of Canterbury. There is a regularly updated calendar of exhibitions and over one thousand permanent objects on display. Entrance is free and there is a café on site.

ADDRESS

18 High Street
CT1 2RA

PHONE

01227 862162

NEAR HERE

Marlowe Theatre (p168)

Westgate Museum (p177)

Waterlane Coffeehouse (p106)

Deal Castle

CULTURE | DEAL | CT14 7BA

Deal Castle is a 16th-century artillery fort, located between Walmer Castle and Sandown Castle. Built by King Henry VIII, it is one of the finest Tudor artillery castles in England. Henry VIII felt the need to protect England from European invasion at this strategic coastal point.

This is a wonderfully well-preserved example of a Tudor coastal fort with an innovative design that was, in its day, state-of-the-art. English Heritage has carefully preserved the architecture and artefacts, and tells the castle's story through interesting displays and guides.

ADDRESS

Marine Road
CT14 7BA

PHONE

01304 372762

NEAR HERE

Walmer Castle (p172)

The Court Yard Oyster Bar (p98)

Popup Cafe (p120)

Walmer Castle

CULTURE | WALMER | CT14 7LJ

Escape the vagaries of modern life at this unique coastal fortress in Kent. Built by Henry VIII in 1540, it became the rural retreat for the Lord Warden of the Cinque Ports, and has played host to the Duke of Wellington, Winston Churchill and the Queen Mother.

There's plenty of military might in evidence at Walmer Castle, with gun ports and heavy cannons lined up on the bastions aimed out towards the continent. Don't miss Wellington's bedroom including his original Wellington boots, the camp bed from which he planned vital campaigns, and the armchair in which he died.

ADDRESS
Kingsdown Road
CT14 7LJ

PHONE
01304 364288

NEAR HERE
The Court Yard Oyster Bar (p9
Deal Castle (p171)
The Black Douglas (p129)

Hever Castle

Hever Castle began as a country house built in the 13th century and was home to the Boleyn family from 1462 - 1539 including Anne Boleyn, the second queen consort of King Henry VIII. The castle fell into disrepair in the early 1900s. Much of what you see is the result of the efforts of William Waldorf Astor, who used his fortune to restore and extend the Castle in the early 20th century.

The panelled rooms house what is regarded as 'one of the best collections of Tudor portraits after the National Portrait Gallery' by David Starkey. The grounds of the castle include a yew maze and a water maze, the object of which is to get to the centre without getting wet.

ADDRESS
Hever Road, Hever
TN8 7NG

PHONE
01732 865224

NEAR HERE
The Tulip Tree (p127)
Leicester Arms (p68)
The Wheatsheaf (p64)

Upnor Castle

CULTURE | ROCHESTER | ME2 4XG

Upnor Castle is an Elizabethan artillery fort located on the west bank of the River Medway. This attractive turreted castle is set in the picturesque village of Upnor within an area backed by rolling, wooded hills. The fort was intended to protect both the dockyard and ships of the Royal Navy anchored in the Chatham Dockyard which is a short distance downriver. It entirely failed at this task in 1667, when the Dutch sailed past it to burn or capture the English fleet at anchor.

The gatehouse and main body of this rare example of an Elizabethan artillery fort are open for viewing and for a nominal charge.

ADDRESS
Upnor Road
ME2 4XG

PHONE
0370 333 1181

NEAR HERE
The Deaf Cat (p131)
The Seaplane Works (p131)
Olive e Capperi Trattoria (p99)

Rochester Castle

CULTURE | ROCHESTER | ME1 1SW

Strategically placed astride the London Road, guarding an important crossing of the River Medway, this imposing fortress has a complex history of destruction and rebuilding. Today it stands as a proud reminder of the history of Rochester along with the cathedral and cobbled streets.

Its Norman tower-keep of Kentish ragstone was built around 1127 by William of Corbeil, Archbishop of Canterbury. In 1215, garrisoned by rebel barons, the castle endured an epic siege by King John. Rebuilt under Henry III and Edward I, the castle remained as a viable fortress until the sixteenth century.

ADDRESS

Castle Hill
ME1 1SW

PHONE

01634 332901

NEAR HERE

Upnor (p174)

Olive e Capperi Trattoria (p99)

The George Vaults (p93)

St Mildred's Church

CULTURE | TENTERDEN | TN30 6AT

St Mildred's Church is the only surviving pre-Conquest church. Highlights include a beamed roof dating from the 1300s, medieval woodcarvings and a font from 1420.

The register within the church dates back to 1559 while the vibrant stained glass windows were installed at the east end of All Saints' Chapel and at the west end of the nave in 1959.

ADDRESS
Church Road
TN30 6AT

PHONE
01580 761591

NEAR HERE
Nutmeg Cafe (p115)
Old Dairy Brewery (p31)
Silcocks farm Shop (152)

Westgate Towers Museum

CULTURE | CANTERBURY | CT1 2BX

Westgate Towers Museum in Canterbury is a 60-foot high medieval gatehouse that is also the largest surviving city gate in England. Built of Kentish ragstone around 1379 by Archbishop Sudbury, it is the last survivor of Canterbury's seven medieval gates.

Visitors can explore its rich history and take in the spectacular views of the city from the battlements viewpoint. Also part of the museum are the original felons' cells built c1830 in the gaol extension and the 1907 police station cells on the ground floor, currently part of The Pound Bar and Kitchen.

ADDRESS

St Peters Place
CT1 2BX

PHONE

01227 458629

NEAR HERE

Boho (p130)

Refectory Kitchen (p94)

Café Mauresque (p129)

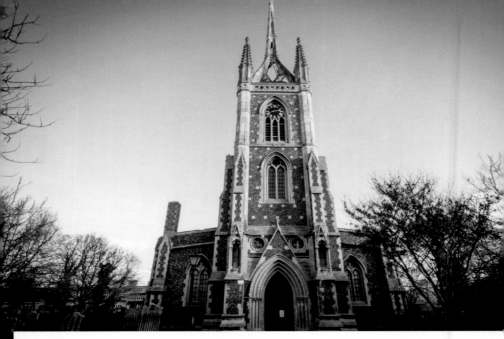

St Mary's Church Faversham

CULTURE | FAVERSHAM | ME13 8GZ

St Mary of Charity is a striking flint church that is said to be the final resting place of King Stephen's bones, after his tomb in Faversham Abbey was ransacked during the Reformation. The church features an unusual corona spire, added in the late 18th century after the original medieval spire was destroyed.

In addition to the monumental brasses, painted Tudor tombs and array of characters, animals and mythological beasts carved out of wood, there is 'one of the most significant medieval artefacts in Britain'. The octagonal column covered entirely with vivid paintings dating back to 1306 is stunning.

ADDRESS
Church Street
ME13 8GZ

PHONE
01795 532592

NEAR HERE
Jittermugs (p103)
The Dirty Habit (p55)
Leeds Castle (p164)

Notes

Tried our app?

bestofengland.com/app

St Martins Church

CULTURE | CANTERBURY | CT1 1PW

St Martin's Church in Canterbury is claimed to be the oldest church in the English-speaking world, which has been used continuously since around 597AD. It was at this church that St. Augustine set up his mission when arriving from Rome with the hope of converting the English.

It is often called the first church of the Anglican Communion. Part Roman, part Saxon and part Medieval, the churchyard contains the graves of many notable local families and well known people including Thomas Sidney Cooper, RA (artist) and Mary Tourtel, the creator of Rupert Bear.

ADDRESS	PHONE
North Holmes Road	01227 768072
CT1 1PW	

Chappell Contemporary

CULTURE | WHITSTABLE | CT5 1DD

Chappell Contemporary Gallery in Whitstable is a new addition to the lively arts scene and shows work by both established and emerging artists. They specialise in signed limited edition prints as well as offering unique originals. Their artists show and sell internationally.

Set up in 2015 by Paula Chappell, this contemporary space displays and sells an interesting curation of colourful and vibrant original designs, beautifully suspended by wires. Set against an interior of stripped wooden flooring and deer skulls, Chappell Contemporary contains some unique artwork.

ADDRESS	PHONE
30 Oxford Street	01227 637329
CT5 1DD	

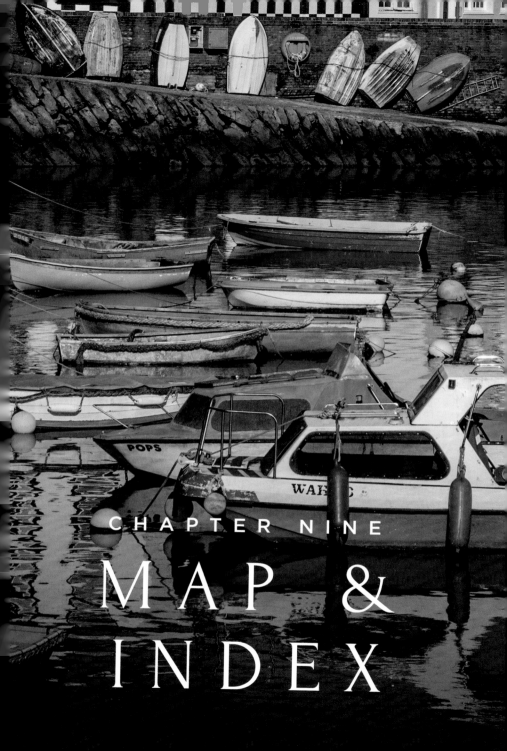

CHAPTER NINE

MAP &
INDEX

INDEX

INDEX

MORNING

Dungeness is a desolate and unique location. With National N
Reserve status, due to the rich and diverse wildlife that thrives here
also one of the largest shingle landscapes in the world. Walk alor
blustery shore line with the monolithic nuclear power station r
imposingly from behind. A multitude of contemporary and aw
winning architect designed properties are emerging here and
unusual places to stay for visitors.

LUNCH TIME

Incredible views can be enjoyed over lunch at Rocksalt. This h
acclaimed modern restaurant overlooks the busy fishing harbou
specialises in seafood, with the day's catch provided by local fishe
wherever possible. This sleek glass structure is cantilevered of
harbour wall and provides a sophisticated addition to this seaside to

AFTERNOON

Folkestone has recently undergone a regeneration process and h
emerging arts scene. Take a walk along the harbour and watch busy
fishermen at work and then visit The Wing, owned by the Batt
Britain Memorial Trust. The building was constructed to mimi
shape of a Spitfire wing and is an interactive, educational space to
about this combat of the Second World War.

EVENING

Luben's pizza offers a buzzy dining experience with authentic, arti
pizzas prepared in their wood-fired oven. This contemporary resta
is light and airy with a relaxed ambience. For after-dinner drinks
to The Pullman with its candlelit tables, roaring fire and casual vibe

MORNING

Breakfast at The Goods Shed, Canterbury is a must. This is a daily farmers' market, providing the best quality produce from Kent's 'Garden of England'. Walk through the city and immerse yourself in its many landmark architectural structures, from the cathedral, Roman city wall, Norman castle and the ruins of St Augustine's Abbey, which are all worth visiting for their enthralling history.

LUNCH TIME

Canterbury offers many highly regarded eateries, tucked away down the medieval streets and along the riverside. For the more carnivorous, try Pork & Co., a casual restaurant serving free-range, fourteen hour slow roast pork on homemade brioche buns. The traceability and welfare of the meat are key. For a more formal dining experience, Chef Dev Biswal has won multiple awards for his Ambrette Restaurant, which offers an exotic fine dining menu.

AFTERNOON

Head to Whitstable and grab a coffee from Whitstable Coffee Company and take a long walk down the pretty beach. The town has been celebrated for its seafood since Roman times and today, in the harbourside fish market, fishermen still showcase and sell their abundant daily catch on ice.

EVENING

Whitstable is a haven for seafood enthusiasts and one of its oldest and most renowned restaurants is Wheelers. Known for its exceptional food, it has a tiny dining room next to its oyster and seafood bar. The atmosphere is unique and it feels as though you're dining in an old fisherman's cottage, with its modest, traditional interior and nautical references.

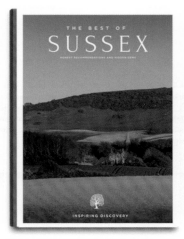

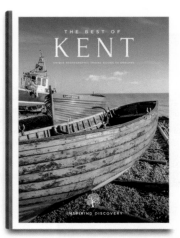

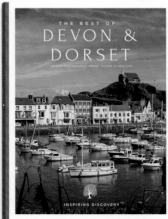

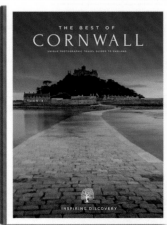

Meet the family

Honest Recommendations & Hidden Gems

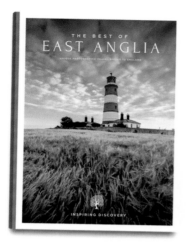

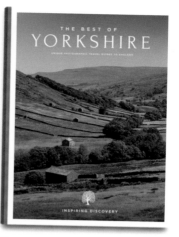

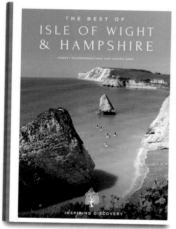

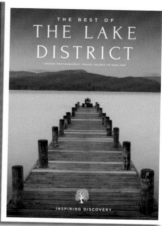

Enjoy 10% off your next purchase using the code: "bestoffriends"

www.bestofengland.com/books

BEST OF ENGLAND

INSPIRING DISCOVERY

About Best of England
Honest Recommendations & Hidden Gems

What is Best of England?

Best of England is a curated collection of travel recommendations. Each one is researched and has been visited and photographed by a member of the Best of England team.

Authenticity & integrity

None of the businesses in this travel guide have paid to be included and we visit every business that we recommend. This guide is based on our own experiences and opinions. We think honesty is a really important part of what we are trying to achieve.

Local knowledge is key

We believe there is nothing better than local knowledge. That's why we speak to the people that live there to find out where to go.

Quality is everything

Quality is behind everything we do and we will never compromise on the recommendations we make. We worry about the details from the thickness of the paper to the size of each font we use and we hope that this effort is reflected in the quality of our products.

Great content comes first

We use our photography to tell a story for each of the businesses we recommend. We want to bring each one to life and inspire our readers to visit themselves.

Tell us what you think

We are always on the look out for ways to improve. Feedback is really important to us in order to make the best product possible. If you have any suggestions or feedback then please let us know via email to **info@bestofengland.com**

The Best of England App

If you like our books then you will love our app.

The app includes all of the great content that
features in this book and much more.
Try it for free. Available for iOS and Android phones.

Find out more at

bestofengland.com/app

The Best of England Boxset

All 8 of our travel guides in a beautiful case. Including:

1. Best of Sussex
2. Best of Kent
3. Best of Devon & Dorset
4. Best of Cornwall

5. Best of Yorkshire
6. Best of East Anglia
7. Best of Lake District & Cumbria
8. Best of Isle of Wight & Hampshire

Find out more at

bestofengland.com/boxset

Are you a hotel or B&B owner?

We are adding an accommodation chapter to the next edition of this guide. If you would like your hotel to be considered, please get in touch.

Find out more at

bestofengland.com/hotels

Notes

Tried our app?

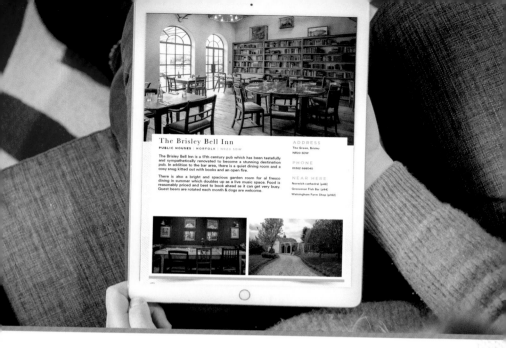

Did you know this guide is also available as an ebook?

The same great content but in a handy PDF to keep on your phone, tablet or laptop.

Find out more at

bestofengland.com/ebooks